C000126462

THE BARBER INSTITUTE OF FINE ARTS

THE BARBER
INSTITUTE
OF FINE ARTS

HANDBOOK

Paul Spencer-Longhurst

THE UNIVERSITY OF BIRMINGHAM

Front cover: *Portrait of a Carmelite prior*, Peter Paul Rubens
Back cover: *King George I on horseback*, Workshop of John Nost the elder

Frontispiece: *Portrait of Lady Barber,* James Jebusa Shannon

Copyright © 1999 The Trustees of the Barber Institute of Fine Arts, The University of Birmingham

Project Management: Magnolia Concept, Warwickshire
Typeset by: Set Two, Cambridgeshire
Printed by: W & G Baird Ltd, Northern Ireland
ISBN 0 7044 20937

CONTENTS

INTRODUCTION

This Handbook lists all works of art currently in the collections of the Barber Institute of Fine Arts. It replaces the earlier handbooks of 1949, 1983 and 1993 and the catalogue of the Institute's collection published by Cambridge University Press in 1952. In addition to being more up-to-date than these, it is the most extensively illustrated catalogue of the collection ever issued and reproduces virtually all the major items in the Institute. For reasons of space, however, it contains only selected illustrations of the extensive holdings of British satirical and portrait drawings and none of the prints, coins, seals and weights, or the works of art inherited from the Barber family estate. A complementary volume, illustrating over 100 of the finest works in the Institute in colour, was published by Scala Publishers Ltd in 1999.

The Barber Institute was founded by Dame Martha Constance Hattie Barber in 1932 in memory of her husband, Sir William Henry Barber, Bt, a solicitor and property developer in Birmingham, who died in 1927. The Institute was created 'for the study and encouragement of art and music' and also houses the University's Departments of History of Art and Music. It is administered by a charitable Trust, the beneficiary of which is the University of Birmingham, and housed in a building designed by Robert Atkinson FRIBA and officially opened by Queen Mary in 1939, six years after Lady Barber's death.

By the terms of the Trust Deed, the collection was intended to comprise 'works of art or beauty of exceptional or outstanding merit and comprising pictures painted not later than the end of the 19th Century furniture tapestries needlework lace mediaeval manuscripts finely printed books and other works of art of such merit as aforesaid (but not pottery or china)'. Of these restrictions, the clause referring to 'the end of the 19th Century' was altered by the Trustees in 1967 to make it possible for them to acquire more recent works of art, providing these are at least 30 years old.

With several notable exceptions, all works in the collection have been purchased by the Trustees, advised by the successive Directors of the Institute: Thomas Bodkin (1935-52), Sir Ellis Waterhouse (1952-70), Hamish Miles (1970-90) and Richard Verdi (1990-). In recent years, however, four major works have been acquired with generous assistance from H. M. Treasury through tax remission. Since 1992, several important acquisitions have been aided by substantial contributions from the Heritage Lottery Fund, the National Art Collections Fund, the Museums and Galleries Commission/Victoria and Albert Museum Purchase Grant Fund, the National Heritage Memorial Fund and the Friends of the Barber Institute of Fine Arts. In two cases works have been bought jointly, with the National Gallery and Birmingham Museums and Art Gallery respectively.

This Handbook has been compiled by the Senior Curator of the Institute, Paul Spencer-Longhurst. In accomplishing this task, he has inevitably drawn extensively upon previous publications of the collection and upon the knowledge and assistance of his predecessors and colleagues at the Institute. In expressing my gratitude to him for the present volume, I am also acknowledging the great indebtedness of both of us to those earlier members of the Institute's staff who were instrumental in creating and investigating this outstanding collection.

Richard Verdi
Director

ABBREVIATIONS

BI 1952	*Catalogue of the paintings, drawings & miniatures in the Barber Institute of Fine Arts*, 1952.
BMAG	Birmingham Museums and Art Gallery
BMAG 1991	Exhibition catalogue, Birmingham Museums and Art Gallery, *French Impressionism: treasures from the Midlands*, 1991
Burl. Mag.	Burlington Magazine
c.l.	centre left
c.r.	centre right
exh. cat.	exhibition catalogue
G.B.A.	*Gazette des Beaux-Arts*
Hind	A.M. Hind, *A catalogue of Rembrandt's etchings*, 1924
Inv. No.	inventory number
l.c.	lower centre
l.l.	lower left
l.r.	lower right
l.r.c.	lower right centre
Lugt	F. Lugt, *Les marques de collections de dessins & d'estampes*, 1921
MM 1986	Exhibition catalogue, London, Morton Morris & Co., *Master drawings in the Barber Institute*, 1986
n.	note
RA 1998	Exhibition catalogue, London, Royal Academy, *Art treasures of England: the regional collections*, 1998
u.c.	upper centre
u.l.	upper left
u.r.	upper right

Abbreviations pertaining specifically to prints are listed at the beginning of the relevant section (p. 127). Measurements are given height before width throughout.

ACKNOWLEDGEMENTS

Among the numerous contributors to the preparation of this edition, the compiler particularly wishes to thank Sue Fryer, Sarah Jennings, Yvonne Locke, John McDill, Karen Parker, Frances Smith, Richard Verdi and Sophie Wilson.

PAINTINGS

Ascribed to
AMBERGER, Christoph
German, c. 1500-62
Portrait of a man

Inscribed l.r.: 130
Oil on wood, 59.8 x 50.2 cm.
Inv. No. 46.6

Painted c. 1530/40.

After
ANDREA del Sarto
Italian, 1486-1530
The Madonna and Child with the infant St John

Oil on wood, 55.3 x 39 cm.
Inv. No. 46.1

J. Shearman, *Andrea del Sarto*, II, 1965, no 59 (i).

A reduced early copy of the lost fresco painted for a tabernacle at the Porta a Pinti, Florence.

AUBRY, Étienne
French, 1745-81

Paternal love

Oil on canvas, 78.7 x 101.5 cm.
Inv. No. 62.10

D. Diderot, *Salons*, ed. J. Seznec, IV,
1967, *Salon de 1775*, no. 175.

Owned in 1775 by comte d'Angiviller,
Director General of Royal Buildings.
Engraved by J.-C. Le Vasseur
(died 1816).

Ascribed to
BARONZIO, Giovanni
Italian, active mid-14th century

The Angel of the Annunciation (top)
*The Nativity and Annunciation to the
Shepherds* (centre)

The Adoration of the Magi (bottom)

Tempera on wood, 44.3 x 20.3 cm.,
including original gabled frame
Inv. No. 42.10

The left wing of a diptych; its counterpart
is in the Galleria Nazionale delle Marche,
Urbino. The panels have also been
ascribed to the Master of Verucchio.

BASCHENIS, Evaristo
Italian, 1617-77

Still-life with musical instruments

Signed l.l.: EVARISTUS/BASCHENIS/
F./BERGOMI
Oil on canvas, 95.5 x 129 cm.
Inv. No. 97.5

RA 1998, no. 312.

Baschenis was the greatest still-life
painter in 17th century Italy. The picture
is a *vanitas*, intended as a reminder of
the futility of earthly accomplishments
and the inevitability of death. Painted
c. 1660.

BASSANO, Jacopo da Ponte, called
Italian, c. 1510-92

The Adoration of the Magi

Oil on canvas, 94.3 x 130 cm.
Inv. No. 78.1

E. Arslan, *I Bassano*, 1960, pp. 105-7,
170 (then in the P. Harris collection);
exh. cat., Bassano del Grappa, Museo
Civico, and elsewhere, *Jacopo Bassano*,
1992-3, under no. 27; RA 1998, no. 288.

Painted in the later 1560s. There are
several other versions of the subjects by
Bassano, of which the closest are in the
Kunsthistorisches Museum, Vienna, the
Hermitage, St Petersburg, and the Fogg
Art Museum, Cambridge, Mass.

BECCAFUMI, Domenico
Italian, 1486?-1551

Reclining nymph

Oil on wood, 71.7 x 138 cm.,
including fictive frame
Inv. No. 62.6

D. Sanminiatelli, *Beccafumi*, 1967,
no. 14.

Probably part of the bedchamber
furnishings painted in about 1519
for Francesco di Camillo Petrucci of
Siena. The subject seems intended
as Venus and Cupid.

(recto)

BEER, Jan de
Early Netherlandish, c. 1475-after 1520

Joseph and the Suitors (recto)
The Nativity (verso)

Oil on wood, 137 x 137 cm.
Inv. No. 51.5

D.C. Ewing, *Jan de Beer*, I, 1978, no. 11.

Painted c. 1515/20 as part of a composite altarpiece, now lost. Two other paintings apparently from it, *The Birth of the Virgin* and *The Annunciation*, are in the Museo Thyssen–Bornemisza, Madrid.

(verso)

BELLANGÉ, Hippolyte
French, 1800-66

The entry of Bonaparte into Milan

Inscribed l.r.: Eug. Delacroix
Oil on canvas, 44.4 x 60.3 cm.
Inv. No. 53.1

L. Johnson, *G.B.A.*, 6e période, LXIV, 1964, pp. 177-82.

The event occurred on 15 May 1796. The attribution to Bellangé rests on his lithograph in A.V. Arnault's *Vie politique et militaire de Napoléon*, 1822 [see Prints, p. 128].

BELLINI, Giovanni
Italian c. 1430-1516

St. Jerome in the wilderness

Signed on cartellino: IHOVANES
BELINUS
Tempera on wood, 44 x 22.9 cm.
Inv. No. 49.1

R. Pallucchini, *Giovanni Bellini*,
1959, p. 127(5); G. Robertson,
Giovanni Bellini, 1968, pp. 15-17;
R. Goffen, *Giovanni Bellini*, 1989,
pp. 4-8.

Generally dated c. 1450, this is Bellini's
earliest signed work. He returned to the
subject several times.

[BELLINI, Giovanni]

Portrait of a boy

Signed and dated : OPUS BELLINI
IOANNIS VENETI/NONALITER
Tempera on wood, 38 x 23 cm.
Inv. No. 46.11

G. Robertson, *Giovanni Bellini*, 1968,
pp. 106-7; R. Goffen, *Giovanni Bellini*,
1989, pp. 202-4; G. Benedicente,
Paragone, XLIII, 513, Nov. 1992,
pp. 3-9.

Possibly painted in the 1470s. The
inscription may be translated: 'The work
of Giovanni Bellini, the Venetian, not
otherwise'.

BICCI di Lorenzo
Italian, 1373-1452

St Romuald

Inscribed on book: 'Pater meum
Romualde ottimus eremita intercede
λ domino pro mihi [illegible]
requiescant ī pace'. Further illegible
inscriptions are on the papers held by
the saint below the frame.
Tempera on wood, 34.3 x 22.8 cm.
Inv. No. 50.6

R. Offner, *Burl. Mag.*, XLIII, 1933,
p. 170, n. 15 (then in the H. Harris
collection); G. Kaftal, *Iconography
of the saints in Tuscan painting*,
1952, pp. 895-8.

St Romuald (died 1027) founded
a hermitage at Camaldoli, east of
Florence, in allusion to which he
holds the model of an abbey. The
inscription is an invocation: 'My
father Romuald, most excellent
hermit, intercede with the Lord
for me [...] may they rest in peace'.

BONNARD, Pierre
French, 1867-1947

The dolls' dinner party

Signed l.l.: Bonnard
Oil on canvas, 37.4 x 45.5 cm.
Inv. No. 63.2

J. and H. Dauberville, *Bonnard*, I,
1965, no. 283; BMAG 1991, p. 56.

Painted c. 1903, this is one of several
intimate scenes of family meals by
the artist.

BORDONE, Paris
Italian, 1500-71

Mythological scene

Oil on wood, 42 x 96 cm.
Inv. No. 61.3

G. Canova, *Paris Bordon*, 1964,
p. 119 (then in the W.H. Woodward
collection).

Possibly painted in the 1530s,
the panel may have been one
of a decorative series. The
subject seems to be a rural idyll,
with reminiscences of Apollo
and the Muses.

Studio of
BOTTICELLI, Sandro
Italian c. 1445-1510

*The Madonna and Child with the
infant St John*

Tempera on canvas, 130.7 x 91.4 cm.
Inv. No. 43.10

R. Lightbown, *Sandro Botticelli*, II,
1978, p. 140 under C 45.

The figures are repeated in reverse
in a painting in the Palazzo Pitti,
Florence, also from Botticelli's
studio. Both versions were painted
in the 1490s.

BOUDIN, Eugène Boudin
French, 1824-98

A beach near Trouville

Signed, inscribed and dated l.r.:
E. Boudin 95/Trouville/
11 Octobre 95
Oil on canvas, 54.3 x 81.2 cm.
Inv. No. 51.1

R. Schmit, *Eugène Boudin,
1824-1898*, III, 1973, no. 3500;
BMAG 1991, p. 38.

The view is probably taken from
Hennequeville, looking across the
mouth of the Seine towards Le Havre.

BREENBERGH, Bartholomeus
Dutch, 1598-1657

Joseph distributing corn in Egypt

Signed and dated l.l.: Barts
Breenburgh fecit/Ano. 1655
Oil on canvas, 110.5 x 90 cm.
Inv. No. 63.1

M. Röthlisberger, *Bartholomeus Breenbergh*, 1981, no. 231.

The replica of a picture dated 1654 in a private collection. The subject is taken from *Genesis*, xliii. The granary behind Joseph u.r. is based on the Roman church of Sta Maria in Aracoeli.

BRUEGHEL, Pieter the younger
Early Netherlandish, 1564/5-1637/8

Two peasants binding faggots

Oil on wood, 36.2 x 27.3 cm.
Inv. No. 44.11

G. Marlier, *Pierre Brueghel le jeune*, 1969, pp. 165-6; exh. cat., Brussels, Palais des Beaux-Arts, *Bruegel, une dynastie de peintres*, 1980, under no. 94.

The subject was treated by the artist several times. Its full meaning remains mysterious, but it may illustrate a proverb or a season of the year.

CALRAET, Abraham van
Dutch, 1642-1722

Horses and cattle in a landscape

Signed l.r.: AC:
Oil on wood, 36 x 53.3 cm.
Inv. No. 59.3

CANALETTO, Giovanni Antonio Canal, called
Italian, 1697-1768

The Loggetta, Venice

Oil on canvas, 45.5 x 75.4 cm.
Inv. No. 54.1

W.G. Constable, *Canaletto*,
revised J.G. Links, II, 1976, no. 39.

Cut down on all sides. Rising from Sansovino's Loggetta is the base of the Campanile. This was painted out, perhaps when the picture was cut, and reappeared as a result of cleaning in 1964.

CAPPELLE, Jan van de
Dutch, 1623/5-79

Boats on ruffled water

Oil on canvas, 71 x 63.5 cm.
Inv. No. 43.1

C. Hofstede de Groot, *A catalogue raisonné [...] of Dutch painters of the seventeenth century*, VII, 1923, no. 129 i.

Probably an early work. The view is of the River Waal near its confluence with the Maas.

CASTELLO, Valerio
Italian, 1624-59

The Madonna and Child with Saints Peter and Paul appearing to St Bruno.

Oil on canvas, 118 x 145.5 cm.
Inv. No. 61.2

C. Manzitti, *Valerio Castello*, 1972, no. 160.

Perhaps painted in the early 1650s. The vision of St Bruno (died 1101, canonized 1623) is combined with allusions – the mitre and crozier – to his refusal of the see of Reggio.

CASTIGLIONE, Giovanni Benedetto
Italian, 1609-64
Rebecca led by the Servant of Abraham
Oil on canvas, 150 x 194.5 cm.
Inv. No. 67.5

Exh. cat., Philadelphia Museum of Art,
*Giovanni Benedetto Castiglione, master
draughtsman of the Italian baroque*, 1971,
p. 33 and under no 59.

Painted c. 1650. The subject seems to be
the journey of Rebecca to become the wife
of Isaac (*Genesis*, xxiv). An old copy is in
the Musée des Beaux-Arts, Bordeaux.

CAVALLINO, Bernardo
Italian, 1616-56
St Catherine of Alexandria
Oil on canvas, 71.7 x 59 cm.
Inv. No. 65.8

Exh. cats., London, Royal Academy,
*Painting in Naples from Caravaggio to
Giordano*, 1982, no. 32; Cleveland
Museum of Art and elsewhere, *Bernardo
Cavallino of Naples, 1616-1656*, 1984,
no. 72.

Probably painted in the later 1640s.
St Catherine is reputed to have lived in
the early 4th century, and to have been
executed by the Roman emperor
Maxentius.

CESARI, Giuseppe, Il Cavaliere
d'Arpino
Italian, 1568-1640
St Lawrence among the poor and sick
Oil on canvas, 61.5 x 73.5 cm.
Inv. No. 88.1

A modello for one of two frescoes
showing scenes from the life of St
Lawrence (martyred 258), formerly in
the church of S. Lorenzo in Damaso,
Rome. They were executed 1588-9. The
subject is based mainly on *The Golden
Legend*, cxv. There is a related drawing
in the Fitzwilliam Museum, Cambridge,
and workshop copies of both frescoes are
in a Roman private collection.

CHAMPAIGNE, Phillippe de
French, 1602-74

The Vision of St Juliana of Mont Cornillon

Oil on canvas, 47.5 x 38.7 cm.
Inv. No. 63.4

B. Dorival, *Philippe de Champaigne 1602-1674*, II, 1976, no. 128.

St Juliana (1191/2-1258) had a vision of a stain on the moon as a symbol of the imperfection of the Church's year. This led to the institution of the feast of Corpus Christi. Etched by J. Morin (died 1650).

CIMA da Conegliano, Giovanni Battista
Italian, 1459/60-1517/18

Christ on the Cross with the Virgin and St John the Evangelist

Tempera on wood, 82.5 x 115.2 cm.
Inv. No. 38.4

P. Humfrey, *Cima da Conegliano*, 1983, no. 20.

Probably from the earlier half of Cima's career. The background scenes are by an assistant.

CLAUDE Gellée, called Le Lorrain
French, 1600-82

Pastoral landscape

Traces of signature and date l.r.c.: 164[5?]
Oil on canvas, 101.5 x 134 cm.
Inv. No. 53.6

M. Röthlisberger, *Claude Lorrain, the paintings*, I, 1961, no. LV 93.

Claude's personal record of the composition is no. 93 in the *Liber Veritatis* (British Museum). A drawing for the group of cattle to the right is recorded (present location unknown). Engraved by F. Vivares, 1741.

Imitator of
CONSTABLE, John
British, 1776-1837
The Glebe Farm

Oil on canvas, 99 x 124.5 cm.
Inv. No. 40.2

R Hoozee, *L'opera completa di John Constable*, 1979, no. 694.

Apparently derived from a mezzotint by David Lucas, based on one of three paintings Constable made of the subject. This is now in the Tate Gallery (no. 1274). The mezzotint was published in the 5th number of *English Landscape Scenery* in 1832.

COROT, Jean-Baptiste-Camille
French, 1796-1875

Landscape with distant mountains

Sale stencil l.r.: VENTE COROT
Oil on canvas, 18 x 29.8 cm.
Inv. No. 70.3

A. Robaut, *L'oeuvre de Corot*, II, 1905, no. 549; exh. cat., London, South Bank Centre, *Corot*, 1991, no. 23.

Datable c. 1840-5 and painted either in the Limousin or the Auvergne. Acquired at Corot's posthumous sale by the artist Henri Fantin-Latour (1836-1904).

Ascribed to
COROT

Wooded landscape with a pond

Incised signature l.r.: C COROT
Oil on canvas, 46.4 x 74.1 cm.
Inv. No. 40.3

Most nearly accords with Corot's style of the mid-1830s and may relate to a drawing of Le Martinet dated 1836 in the Metropolitan Museum, New York.

COURBET, Jean-Désiré-Gustave
French, 1819-77

The sea-arch at Étretat

Signed l.l.: G. Courbet
Oil on canvas, 76.2 x 123.1 cm.
Inv. No. 47.2

R. Lindon, *G.B.A.*, 6e période, LI, 1958, pp. 353-60; exh. cat., Edinburgh, National Gallery of Scotland, *Lighting up the landscape*, 1986, no. 78; BMAG 1991, p. 10.

Painted in 1869. Étretat, near Le Havre, was popularized by writers and painters in the mid-19th century. Courbet painted at least four more versions of its sea-arch, the spectacular *Porte d'Aval*, in the same year.

CRESPI, Giuseppe Maria
Italian, 1665-1747

The flea

Oil on canvas, 49.5 x 38 cm.
Inv. No. 65.3

M.P. Merriman, *Giuseppe Maria Crespi*, 1980, no. 248; exh. cat., Fort Worth, Kimbell Art Museum, *Giuseppe Maria Crespi and the emergence of genre painting in Italy*, 1986, under no. 21.

Probably painted c. 1715-20. One of seven known variations by Crespi or his assistants on the theme of a young woman searching her bosom for a flea. A replica is in the Art Institute of Chicago.

CROME, John and John Berney
British, 1768-1821 and 1794-1842

A view near Harwich

Oil on canvas, 114.3 x 96.5 cm.
Inv. No. 39.21

D. and T. Clifford, *John Crome*, 1968, no. P 124.

The location is traditional. Much overpainted by the younger Crome, probably c. 1832.

CUYP, Aelbert
Dutch, 1620-91

Huntsmen halted

Oil on canvas, 92.7 x 130.8 cm.
Inv. No. 59.5

S. Reiss, *Aelbert Cuyp*, 1975, no. 122.

Probably painted in the early 1650s. The huntsmen are the three sons of Cornelis van Beveren (1591-1663), a major patron of the artist.

DAUBIGNY, Charles-François
French, 1817-78

Seascape

Sale stamp l.l.: VENTE DAUBIGNY
Oil on canvas, 84 x 146.5 cm.
Inv. No. 72.1

R. Hellebranth, *Charles-François Daubigny 1817-1878*, 1977, no. 577; exh. cat., Edinburgh, National Gallery of Scotland, *Lighting up the landscape*, 1986, no. 71; BMAG 1991, p. 12.

Probably painted c. 1867. The traditional title, *Taliferme en Bretagne*, first used in 1878, is problematic as there is nowhere in Brittany called Taliferme.

Attributed to
DE DREUX, Alfred
French, 1810-60

A horse in a landscape

Oil on canvas, 34.3 x 44.4 cm.
Inv. No. 54.7

The painting has also been attributed to Géricault and Carle Vernet (1758-1836).

DEGAS, Hilaire-Germain-Edgar
French, 1834-1917

Jockeys before the race

Signed l.r.: Degas
Oil, essence, gouache and pastel on
paper, 107.3 x 73.7 cm.
Inv. No. 50.2

P.A. Lemoisne, *Degas et son oeuvre*,
1946, no. 649; exh. cat., Edinburgh,
National Gallery of Scotland, *Degas 1879*,
1979, no. 11; BMAG 1991, p. 22; RA
1998, no. 352.

Painted 1878-9 and exhibited at the 4th
Impressionist exhibition (no. 63).

DELACROIX, Ferdinand-Victor-Eugène
French, 1798-1863

St Stephen borne away by his disciples

Signed and dated l.r.: Eug. Delacroix 1862
Oil on canvas, 46.6 x 38 cm.
Inv. No. 62.1

L. Johnson, *The paintings of Eugène
Delacroix*, III, 1986, no. 472; exh. cat.,
Paris, Grand Palais, and elsewhere,
Delacroix, les dernières années, 1998,
no. 140.

The subject is from *The Acts of the Apostles*,
vii: 58 and viii: 2. A larger variant, dated
1853 and shown at the Salon that year, is in
the Musée Municipal, Arras. Two smaller
versions are in private collections.

DENIS, Maurice
French, 1870-1943

Portrait of Monsieur Huc

Signed and dated vertically l.r.: MAUD 92
Oil on millboard, 28.5 x 53.5 cm.
Inv. No. 87.1

Exh. cats., Paris, Pavillon de Marsan,
Exposition rétrospective Maurice Denis,
1924, no. 34; BMAG 1991, p. 54; Lyon,
Musée des Beaux-Arts, and elsewhere,
1994, *Maurice Denis, 1870-1943*, no. 49.

Arthur Huc, one of the earliest patrons of
Denis, was an art critic and the founding
director of the newspaper, *La Dépêche de
Toulouse*. Preliminary drawings for the
picture are in a private collection.

DERAIN, André
French, 1880-1954

Portrait of Bartolomeo Savona

Signed l.r.c.: a. derain
Oil on canvas, 45.7 x 35.4 cm.
Inv. No. 97.1

R. Verdi, *Burl.Mag.*, CXL, May 1998,
pp. 325-7; RA 1998, no. 361.

Acquired with financial assistance from
the Heritage Lottery Fund and the
National Art Collections Fund.

The sitter was a teacher of English from
Palermo. He befriended Derain in
London in 1906 and was painted by him
there between January and March that
year.

DOSSO Dossi
Italian, 1485/90?-1542

*Scenes from the Aeneid: the Sicilian
games*

Oil on canvas, 58.5 x 167.5 cm.
Inv. No. 64.5

Exh. cat., New York, Metropolitan Museum
and elsewhere, *Dosso Dossi*, 1998, pp. 147-53.

The scenes seem to be based loosely on
Virgil's *Aeneid*, book v, lines 67 ff., 94 ff.,
106-7, 605 ff., 657-8, 666, 711 ff. This and
nine other pictures painted in the 1520s
formed the frieze in the *camerino* of duke
Alfonso d'Este at Ferrara. The only two
others surviving are in the National Gallery
of Canada, Ottawa, and the National
Gallery of Art, Washington, D.C.

DUGHET, Gaspard
French, 1615-75

Classical landscape with figures

Oil on canvas, 36.8 x 47 cm.
Inv. No. 69.8

M.N. Boisclair, *Gaspard Dughet*, 1986,
no. 386.

Possibly painted c. 1672-5.

DUJARDIN, Karel
Dutch, 1621/2-78

Pastoral landscape

Signed l.c.: K. DU. JARDIN
Oil on wood, 28 x 34 cm.
Inv. No. 67.2

C. Hofstede de Groot, *Verzeichnis des
Werke des[...]Holländischen Maler,
IX*, 1926, pp. 333-4, no. 155.

Probably painted in the 1650s, after the
artist's return from Italy.

DUSART, Cornelis
Dutch, 1660-1704

The milk seller

Signed and dated l.r.: K. Dusart 1679
Oil on wood, 38.8 x 29.5 cm.
Inv. No. 49.8

K. Lilienfeld in U. Thieme and F.
Becker, *Allgemeines Lexikon der
bildenden Kunst*, X, 1914, p. 224 (then
in the Six collection).

Apparently the artist's earliest dated
work.

DYCK, Anthony van
Flemish, 1599-1641

Ecce Homo

Oil on canvas, 101.5 x 78.7 cm.
Inv. No. 54.4

Exh. cats., Princeton, University Art
Museum, *Van Dyck as religious artist*,
1979, no. 33; Antwerp, Koninklijk Museum
voor Schone Kunsten, and elsewhere, *Van
Dyck, 1599-1641*, 1999, no. 39.

Painted in Italy, very probably in Genoa,
c. 1625-6. The subject derives from *John*,
xix: 5. An earlier oil sketch is in the
Courtauld Institute, London, and a later,
related painting, *The Mocking of Christ*,
is in Princeton University Art Museum.

[DYCK, Anthony van]

Portrait of François Langlois

Oil on canvas, 97.8 x 80 cm.
Inv. No. 97.4/6567

Exh. cat., Antwerp, Koninklijk Museum voor Schone Kunsten, and elsewhere, *Van Dyck, 1599-1641*, 1999, no. 83.

Acquired jointly with the National Gallery and with financial assistance from the Heritage Lottery Fund.

The sitter (1589-1647) was a French engraver, art dealer and publisher and a friend of the artist. Dressed in Arcadian costume as a *savoyard*, he plays a *musette*. Probably painted in London in 1637. A preliminary drawing is in the Institut Néerlandais, Paris.

EARLY NETHERLANDISH
15th century

The Deposition (centre)

Adam and Eve mourning Abel (left)

Joseph's coat shown to Jacob (right)

St Helena (left verso)

St Veronica (right verso)

Oil on wood, triptych, centre panel 53.3 x 42.8 cm; wings 52.5 x 16.7 cm. Inv. No. 60.4

Probably painted in Brussels c. 1470 by a follower of Rogier van der Weyden, perhaps Vrancke van der Stockt (died 1496?). The Old Testament subjects derive from *Genesis*, iv: 8 and xxxvii: 31-4 respectively. The versos of the wings are in grisaille.

(left wing, verso)   (right wing, verso)

FETTI, Domenico
Italian, c. 1588/9-1623

The Blind leading the Blind

Oil on wood, 60.7 x 44.2 cm.
Inv. No. 49.13

P. Askew, *Art Bulletin*, XLIII, 1961,
pp. 36-7, 42-3; exh. cat., London,
National Gallery, *Venetian seventeenth
century painting*, 1979, no. 12.

Painted 1621-2. The composition derives
from the left part of Fetti's horizontal
picture of the same subject in the
Gemäldegalerie, Dresden. A repetition,
probably autograph, is in the collection of
the Duke of Northumberland. Christ's
parable is recorded in *Matthew*, xv: 14
and *Luke*, vi: 39.

FLINCK, Govaert
Dutch, 1615-60

Portrait of a boy

Signed and dated l.r.: G. Flinck. f 1640
Oil on canvas, 129.5 x 102.5 cm.
Inv. No. 40.8

J.W. von Moltke, *Govaert Flinck
1615-1660*, 1965, no. 407;
W. Sumowski, *Gemälde der
Rembrandt-Schüler*, II, 1983, no. 692;
P. Visser and M. Sprunger, *Menno
Simons: places, portraits and progeny*,
1996, no.68.

The identity of the sitter is uncertain, but
he may be David Leeuw (c.1632-1703), a
distant relation of the artist.

GAINSBOROUGH, Thomas
British, 1727-88

The harvest wagon

Oil on canvas, 120.5 x 144.7 cm.
Inv. No. 46.8

J. Hayes, *The landscape paintings of
Thomas Gainsborough*, II, 1982, no. 88;
exh. cat., BMAG and Art Gallery of
Ontario, Toronto, *Thomas Gainsborough,
'The Harvest Wagon'*, 1995, pp. 10-23,
no.1 and passim.

Exhibited at the Society of Artists in 1767
(no. 61). A variant of 1784-5 is in the Art
Gallery of Ontario, Toronto. Two preparatory drawings are in private collections.

[GAINSBOROUGH, Thomas]

Portrait of Giusto Ferdinando Tenducci

Oil on canvas, 76.6 x 64 cm.
Inv. No. 44.3

E.K. Waterhouse, *Gainsborough*, 1958, no. 656; exh. cats., London, Kenwood, *Gainsborough and his musical friends*, 1977, no. 7; Ferrara, Palazzo dei Diamanti, *Thomas Gainsborough*, 1998, no. 16.

Painted c. 1773-5 but unfinished. A more complete variant is in a British private collection, and a version by Gainsborough Dupont (c. 1755-97) is in the Garrick Club, London. Tenducci (c. 1734-90) was a celebrated castrato singer and composer.

[GAINSBOROUGH, Thomas]

Portrait of the Hon. Harriott Marsham

Oil on canvas, 75 x 61 cm.
Inv. No. 46.9

E.K. Waterhouse, *Gainsborough*, 1958, no. 469.

Probably painted in the late 1770s. The sitter (1721-96) was an unmarried daughter of the 1st Baron Romney.

GAUGUIN, Paul
French, 1848-1903

Bathers at Tahiti

Signed and dated l.r.: P. Gauguin 97
Oil on sacking, 73.3 x 91.8 cm.
Inv. No. 49.9

G. Wildenstein, *Gauguin*, I, 1964, no. 564; exh. cats., Washington, D.C., National Gallery of Art, and elsewhere, *The art of Paul Gauguin*, 1988, p. 392, no. 9; BMAG 1991, p. 52; Martigny, Fondation Pierre Giannada, *Gauguin*, 1998, no. 119.

Painted in 1897, during Gauguin's second period in Tahiti.

Ascribed to
GAUGUIN

Landscape at Pont-Aven

Signed and dated l.r.: P. Gauguin 88
Oil on canvas, 66.1 x 100 cm.
Inv. No. 48.12

G. Wildenstein, *Gauguin*, I, 1964,
no. 271.

Another view of the village from the
same point was painted by Gauguin in
1886 (present location unknown). The
handling of paint and compositional
shortcomings of the present picture,
however, give rise to serious doubts
about its authenticity.

GELDER, Arent de
Dutch, 1645-1727

Ahasuerus and Haman

Oil on canvas, 138.5 x 116.8 cm.
Inv. No. 47.3

W. Sumowski, *Gemälde der Rembrandt-
Schüler*, II, 1984, no. 739; Dordrecht,
Dordrechts Museum and elsewhere,
*Arent de Gelder: Rembrandts laatste
leerling*, 1998, no. 16.

The subject is taken from *Esther*, iii: 8-9.

GOGH, Vincent van
Dutch, 1853-90

A peasant woman digging

Oil on canvas, 42 x 32 cm.
Inv. No. 61.8

J.-B. de la Faille, *The works of Vincent
van Gogh*, 1970, no. F 95a; BMAG
1991, p. 42.

Painted at Nuenen near Eindhoven,
in July 1885.

GOSSAERT, Jan, called Mabuse
Early Netherlandish, c. 1478?-1532

Hercules and Deianira

Inscribed u.c.: HERCULES DYANIRA
Dated l.l.: 1517
Oil on wood, 36.8 x 26.6 cm.
Inv. No. 46.10

M.J. Friedländer, *Early Netherlandish painting, VIII: Gossaert and van Orley*, 1972, no. 50; exh. cat., Amsterdam, Rijksmuseum, *Kunst voor de Beeldenstorm*, 1986, no. 1; RA 1998, no. 282.

The reliefs on the seat represent scenes from the Labours of Hercules: his struggle with Antaeus (left), killing of the Nemean Lion, and bearing of the globe for Atlas (right).

GOYEN, Jan van
Dutch, 1596-1656

Landscape in the dunes

Signed and dated l.l.: VG 1631
Oil on wood, 42.5 x 54.5 cm.
Inv. No. 59.4

H.-U. Beck, *Jan van Goyen*, II, 1973, no. 1001.

Attributed to
GREBBER, Pieter Fransz. de
Dutch, c. 1600-52/3

The Angel appearing to Anna

Oil on wood, 38.7 x 29.8 cm.
Inv. No. 51.2

The subject derives from the apocryphal *Gospel of Mary*, iii: 1-2, and *Proto-evangelion*, iv: 1.

GUARDI, Francesco
Italian, 1712-93
A regatta on the Grand Canal, Venice
Oil on canvas, 67 x 92.1 cm.
Inv. No. 41.1
A. Morassi, *Guardi*, I, 1973, no. 305.

HALS, Frans
Dutch, 1581/5-1666
Portrait of a man holding a skull
Inscribed u.r.: ITA MORI/AETAT
SUAE 60
Oil on wood, 94 x 72.5 cm.
Inv. No. 38.6
S. Slive, *Frans Hals*, III, 1974, no. 2;
exh. cat., London, Royal Academy,
Frans Hals, 1990, no. 2.
Painted c. 1610-14, one of the artist's
earliest works. The sitter and coat-of-
arms are unidentified. The *Portrait of
a woman* at Chatsworth is the pendant.

HEEM, Jan Davidsz. de
Dutch, 1606-83/4
Still life with a nautilus cup
Signed and dated u.r.: JDHeem f./
JDHeem f. Ao 1632 [both sets of
initials in monogram]
Oil on wood, 77.5 x 64.7 cm.
Inv. No. 41.2
I. Bergström, *Oud-Holland*, LXXI,
1956, p. 180; exh. cat., Amsterdam,
Rijksmuseum, *Still-life paintings from
the Netherlands 1550-1720*, 1999, no. 29.

HONE, Nathaniel
Irish, 1718-84

Portrait of Charles Lee Lewes

Oil on canvas, 71 x 61 cm.
Inv. No. 59.6

Exh. cat., Nottingham University
Art Gallery, and elsewhere, *Genial
company*, 1987, p. 42.

The sitter (1740-1803) was an actor. He
is shown holding the music of a popular
song, *The Contented Fellow*, first
published in 1767.

INGRES, Jean-Auguste-Dominique
French, 1780-1867

Paolo and Francesca

Signed l.l.: J.INGRES
Oil on canvas, 35 x 28 cm.
Inv. No. 54.6

G. Wildenstein, *Ingres*, 1954, no. 123;
exh. cat., Louisville, J.B. Speed Art
Museum, and elsewhere, *In pursuit of
perfection: the art of J.-A.-D. Ingres*,
1983-4, pp. 70-2, no. 19.

The subject comes from Dante, *Inferno*,
v, lines 127 ff. It was drawn and painted
by Ingres a number of times; the present
picture most nearly resembles a version
in the Musée Condé, Chantilly. Other
versions are in the Musée Turpin de
Crissé, Angers, and the Musée Bonnat,
Bayonne.

ITALIAN

13th century

The Crucifixion

Tempera on wood, 50.8 x 27 cm.
Inv. No. 39.1

R. Longhi, *Opere complete*, VII:
Giudizio sul dugento, 1974, p. 9.

Probably painted in Tuscany towards
the end of the 13th century.

ITALIAN

14th century

Madonna and Child enthroned (centre)

St John the Baptist, with above
The Angel of the Annunciation (left)

St Mary Magdalene, with above
The Madonna Annunciate (right)

Tempera on wood, triptych,
27.2 x 40 cm., including wings.
Inv. No. 60.4

Probably painted in the 1360s/70s in
Venice or Rimini. On the versos of the
wings are fragmentary figures of St
Dominic (left) and an unidentified
female saint (right).

(detail of left
wing, verso)

(detail of right
wing, verso)

ITALIAN
16th century

Madonna and Child

Maiolica plaque, 24.1 x 19 cm.
Inv. No. 54.2

B. Rackham, *Apollo*, XXXVI, 1937, p. 65

From Faenza, or the neighbourhood of Florence. Executed in the early 16th century.

JOHN, Gwen
British, 1876-1939

Mère Poussepin

Oil on canvas, 60.5 x 45.3 cm.
Inv. No. 76.1

C. Langdale, *Gwen John*, 1987, p. 51 and no. 53.

Based on a prayer-card image of Mother Marie Poussepin (1653-1744), who founded the Dominican Sisters of the Presentation of the Blessed Virgin of Tours in 1684. The artist formed an association with the nuns of the order at Meudon, and painted at least six versions of this subject. The present composition was probably painted between 1915 and 1920.

LANCRET, Nicolas
French, 1690-1743

Lovers in a landscape

Oil on canvas, 75.3 x 97.5 cm.
Inv. No. 37.10

A smaller version, on wood, is in the Louvre.

LAWRENCE, Sir Thomas
British, 1769-1830

Portrait of a lady

Oil on canvas, 73.6 x 60.9 cm.
Inv. No. 58.8

K. Garlick, *Sir Thomas Lawrence*,
1989, no. 872.

Painted c. 1790-5.

LÉGER, Fernand
French, 1881-1955

Composition with fruit

Signed and dated l.r.: 38/F. LEGER
Signed and dated on the verso:
Composition aux 2 fruits/38. F LEGER
Oil on canvas, 92 x 65 cm.
Inv. No. 85.1

Exh. cat., London, Annely Juda
Fine Art, *Twenty years. Masterpieces
of the avantgarde*, 1985, no. 25.

Follower of
LE NAIN, Mathieu
French, 1607?-77

The gamesters

Oil on canvas, 85 x 114.3 cm.
Inv. No. 41.8

Exh. cat., Paris, Grand Palais,
Les frères Le Nain, 1978-9, no. 47.

Probably painted in the early 1650s. The
picture is one of a group, including *The
dice players* (Rijksmuseum, Amsterdam)
and *The backgammon players* (Louvre)
by an artist working close to the style
associated with Mathieu Le Nain.

LE SUEUR, Eustache
French, 1616-55

Solomon and the Queen of Sheba

Oil on canvas, 92.7 x 114.9 cm.
Inv. No. 58.7

A. Mérot, *Eustache Le Sueur*, 1987, no. 111.

Painted in 1650 as an overmantel for the Hôtel de Tonnay-Charente, Paris. The subject is taken from *I Kings*, x: 1-2, 19-20 and *II Chronicles*, ix: 1, 17-19. Preliminary drawings are in the National-museum, Stockholm, the Städelsches Kunstinstitut, Frankfurt and the Musée Condé, Chantilly.

MAES, Nicolaes
Dutch, 1634-93

Portrait of a lady

Signed l.l.: N MAES
[the initials in monogram]
Oil on canvas, 113.6 x 89.5 cm.
Inv. No. 44.12

Perhaps a work of the mid-1670s.

MAGRITTE, René
Belgian, 1898-1955

The flavour of tears

Signed l.l.: Magritte
Inscribed and dated on verso:
"LA SAVEUR/DES LARMES"/1948
Oil on canvas, 59.4 x 49.5 cm.
Inv. No. 83.1

D. Sylvester ed., *René Magritte. Catalogue raisonné*, II, 1993, no. 665; exh. cat., Brussels, Royal Museums of Fine Arts of Belgium, *René Magritte 1898-1967*, 1998, no. 154, pp. 158-63.

Another version, almost identical and also dated 1948, is in the Musée d'Art Moderne, Brussels.

MANET, Édouard
French, 1832-83
Portrait of Carolus-Duran
Traces of signature l.l.: Manet
Oil on canvas, 191.8 x 172.7 cm.
Inv. No. 37.12

D. Rouart and D. Wildenstein,
Édouard Manet, I, 1975, no. 245;
BMAG 1991, pp. 14-15.

Begun in the summer of 1876 at
Montgeron, but left unfinished. Emile-
Auguste Carolus-Duran (1838-1917) was
a fashionable portraitist and friend of the
artist. He in turn began a portrait of
Manet (Musée d'Orsay, Paris).

Ascribed to
MASSYS, Quentin
Early Netherlandish, 1465/6-1530
Portrait of an ecclesiastic
Oil on wood, 66.3 x 51 cm.
Inv. No. 43.5

M.J. Friedländer, *Early Netherlandish
painting, VII: Quentin Massys*, 1971,
pp. 89, 95, n. 112.

The identity of the sitter is doubtful; he
was perhaps Jean Carondelet (1468-
1544), a counsellor to the Archduchess
Margaret of Austria in the Government of
the Low Countries.

MASTER OF THE GRISELDA LEGEND
Italian, active c. 1500

Alexander the Great

Inscribed l.c.: ALEXANDER/
QUI PROPRIUS TOTUM SUPERAVI
VIRIBUS ORBEM/EXCUSSI
FLAMMAS CORDE CUPIDINEAS/
NIL IVAT EXTERNIS BELLI
GAUDERE TRIUMPHIS/SI MENS
AEGRA IACET INTERIUS QUE
FURIT
Tempera on wood, arched top,
105.4 x 50.8 cm.
Inv. No. 51.4

R.L. Mode, in *Hortus imaginum; essays in western art*, University of Kansas, 1974, pp. 73-83; A.B. Barriault, *Spalliera paintings of Renaissance Tuscany*, 1994, pp. 149-50.

One of a series of virtuous figures from antiquity, executed to decorate a room in a Sienese palace associated with the Piccolomini family, whose heraldic crescents appear in the hands of the putti supporting the inscription. The latter may be translated as: 'I, Alexander, who conquered the whole world with my own strength, shook off the flames of desire from my heart. It is of no avail to rejoice in the outward triumphs of war if the mind lies sick and rages within'. The literary sources are Plutarch's *Lives: Alexander*, iv: 1-4; xx-xxi; xxii: 5-6; and Valerius Maximus, *Alexander the Great*, iv: 7, ext. 2. Seven other panels from the series are known. Three are ascribed to the present artist: *Artemisia* (Museo Poldi Pezzoli, Milan), *Tiberius Gracchus* (Szépmüvészeti Múzeum, Budapest) and *Eunostos of Tanagra* (National Gallery of Art, Washington D.C.).

MASTER OF THE JUDGEMENT OF PARIS
Italian, active mid-15th century

Daphne pursued by Apollo

Tempera on wood, 47.4 x 53.1 cm.
Inv. No. 50.7a

The subjects of this and of no. 50.7b below derive from Ovid, *Metamorphoses*, i: 452 ff. The panels probably formed the ends of a *cassone* (marriage chest).

[MASTER OF THE JUDGEMENT OF PARIS]

The metamorphosis of Daphne

Tempera on wood, 47.5 x 53.1 cm.
Inv. No. 50.7b

For comment, see above, no. 50.7a.

MASTER OF THE LEGEND OF ST URSULA
Early Netherlandish, active in the later 1480s

Christ on the Cross, with a donor

Oil on wood, 44 x 33 cm.
Inv. No. 60.8

M.J. Friedländer, *Early Netherlandish painting, VIb: Hans Memlinc and Gerard David*, 1971, p. 110, supp. 238; exh. cat., Nuremburg, Germanisches Museum, *Martin Luther und die Reformation in Deutschland*, 1983, no. 488.

MATTEO di Giovanni
Italian, c. 1430?-95

Madonna and Child with St John the Baptist and St Michael the Archangel

Tempera on wood, 57.9 x 40.4 cm.
Inv. No. 44.2

J. Pope-Hennessy, *Sienese quattrocentro painting*, 1947, pp. 8, 18, 29; E.S. Trimpi, *Matteo di Giovanni*, Ann Arbor, UMI, 1987, pp. 111-113, no. 13.

Painted c. 1485-95.

MAZZONI, Sebastiano
Italian, c. 1611-78

The Three Fates

Oil on canvas, arched top, 210.5 x 153.3 cm.
Inv. No. 90.1

Exh. cat., London, Walpole Gallery, *Venetian baroque and rococo paintings*, 1990, no. 3.

Probably painted c. 1670.

MIEL, Jan
Flemish, 1599-1664

The Arch of Constantine, Rome

Oil on canvas, 126.3 x 175.2 cm.
Inv. No. 69.3

T. Kren, *Jan Miel, a Flemish painter in Rome*, II, 1978, no. A 47.

Painted in the 1640s, the picture seems to have been a collaborative venture between Miel, who painted the figures and perhaps the arch, and another artist, possibly Viviano Codazzi or Alessandro Salucci, who painted the architecture. A companion picture, by Gaspard Dughet and Miel, is in the Fitzwilliam Museum, Cambridge.

MILLET, Jean-François
French, 1814-75

A milkmaid

Signed l.r.: J.F. Millet
Oil on canvas, 32.5 x 24 cm.
Inv. No. 77.1

R.L. Herbert, *Revue du Louvre*, XXX,
1980, pp. 16-7, 18, 20; BMAG 1991,
p. 5.

Painted c. 1853. Several variants exist,
notably those in the Louvre, the Palazzo
Communale, Milan, and a private
collection, Los Angeles.

MOLIJN, Pieter
Dutch, 1595-1661

Landscape with a huntsman

Oil on wood, 33 x 54.6 cm.
Inv. No. 52.2

Exh. cat., Hull, Ferens Art Gallery,
*Dutch painting of the seventeenth
century*, 1961, no. 69; H.-U. Beck,
Jan van Goyen, II, 1973, no. 1183 a.

Previously ascribed to Jan van Goyen.

MONET, Claude Oscar
French, 1840-1926

The Church at Varengeville

Signed l.r.: Claude Monet 82
Oil on canvas, 65 x 81.3 cm.
Inv. No. 38.7

D. Wildenstein, *Claude Monet*, II, 1979,
no. 727; BMAG 1991, pp. 32-3; RA
1998, no. 354

One of three pictures of this motif painted
in 1882; the others are in the J.B. Speed
Art Museum, Louisville, and a French
private collection.

MURILLO, Bartolomé Esteban
Spanish, 1617-82

The Marriage Feast at Cana

Oil on canvas, 179 x 235 cm.
Inv. No. 47.9

D. Angulo Iñiguez, *Murillo*, I, 1981, pp. 423-4; II, no. 237; exh. cat., London, Royal Academy, *Bartolomé Esteban Murillo 1617-1682*, 1983, no. 57; D. Kinkead, *Burl. Mag.*, CXXVIII, Feb. 1986. p. 136.

Probably painted c. 1672 for Don Nicolas Omazur, a Flemish silk merchant resident in Seville. The subject is taken from *John*, ii: 1-11.

NERI di Bicci
Italian, 1419-c. 1491

St John the Baptist leaving for the desert

Tempera on wood, 23.8 x 37.8 cm.
Inv. No. 50.5

A. Thomas, *Apollo*, CXLIII, May 1996, pp. 3-7.

Originally part of the predella of an altarpiece commissioned in 1470. Its main panel may have been *The Annunciation*, now in the church of S. Lucia al Borghetto a Tavarnelle Valdipesa. The subject is an elaboration of *Luke*, i: 76 and 80.

ORCHARDSON, Sir William Quiller
Scottish, 1832-1910

Portrait of Lady Orchardson

Oil on canvas, 124.5 x 97.8 cm.
Inv. No. 39.23

Exh. cat., Edinburgh, Royal Scottish Academy and elsewhere, *Sir William Quiller Orchardson, R.A.*, 1972, no 23.

Orchardson married the sitter, Ellen Moxon (c. 1854-1917), in 1873. The present portrait was exhibited at the Royal Academy in 1875 (no. 70). An earlier full-length is in the National Gallery of Scotland, as is *Master Baby* (1886), in which this sitter is shown as the mother.

PELLEGRINI, Giovanni Antonio
Italian, 1675-1741

Judith and her maidservant with the head of Holofernes

Oil on canvas, 124.7 x 102 cm.
Inv. No. 74.1

Exh. cat., London, Royal Academy, and elsewhere, *The glory of Venice*, 1994, no. 40; G. Knox, *Antonio Pellegrini*, 1995, p. 227.

Probably painted c. 1710, when the artist was in England. The subject is taken from *Judith*, xiii: 9-10.

PISSARRO, Camille
French, 1830-1903

The pond at Montfoucault

Signed and dated l.l.: C. Pissarro 1875
Oil on canvas, 73.6 x 92.7 cm.
Inv. No. 55.16

L.R. Pissarro and L. Venturi, *Camille Pissarro*, I, 1939, no. 320; exh. cat., BMAG and elsewhere, *Camille Pissarro*, 1990, pp. 43-5; BMAG 1991, p. 18.

One of several paintings of the pond by Pissarro; a larger, slightly later variant was formerly in the Rosenberg collection, Paris. A related drawing is in the Arkansas Art Centre.

POUSSIN, Nicolas
French, 1594-1665

Tancred and Erminia

Oil on canvas, 75.5 x 99.7 cm.
Inv. No. 38.9

A.F. Blunt, *The paintings of Nicolas Poussin*, 1966, no. 207; exh. cats., BMAG, *Nicolas Poussin, 'Tancred & Erminia'*, 1992, pp. 10-34, no. 7 and passim; Paris, Grand Palais, *Nicolas Poussin 1594-1665*, 1994, no. 49; London, Royal Academy, *Nicolas Poussin*, 1995, no. 26.

Painted c. 1634. The subject is from Tasso's *Gerusalemme liberata*, xix: stanzas 102 ff. The painting is featured in *Sir James Thornhill showing his Poussin to his friends*, attributed to Gawen Hamilton (Beaverbrook Art Gallery, Fredericton, N.B., Canada). An earlier variant is in the Hermitage, St Petersburg. Engraved by G. van der Gucht before 1734. [See also Prints, Gucht, p. 132].

PRETI, Mattia
Italian, 1613-99

The Martyrdom of St. Peter

Oil on canvas, 194.5 x 194.3 cm.
Inv. No. 71.1

Exh. cat., London, Royal Academy, *Painting in Naples 1606-1705*, 1982, no. 103; E. Corace, ed., *Mattia Preti*, 1989, pp. 28, 31, 90, 150.

One of three scenes of martyrdom commissioned by Ferdinand van den Einden, a Flemish merchant in Naples, and painted there c. 1656-60. The companion *Decollation of St Paul* is in the Museum of Fine Arts, Houston, and *The Martyrdom of St Bartholomew* is in the Currier Gallery of Art, Manchester, New Hampshire. A larger variant of the present picture is in the Musée de Peinture et de Sculpture, Grenoble.

PUVIS DE CHAVANNES,
Pierre-Cécile
French, 1824-98

The Beheading of St John the Baptist

Signed and dated l.r.: Puvis de
Chavannes/14 Xbre 1869
Oil on canvas, 124.5 x 166 cm.
Inv. No. 56.5

Exh. cat., Amsterdam, Van Gogh
Museum, and elsewhere, *Pierre Puvis de
Chavannes*, 1994, no. 57; J. Leighton and
D. Bomford, *Burl.Mag.*, CXXXVIII,
Sept. 1996, pp. 592-8.

Exhibited at the Paris Salon of 1870
(no. 2346). A larger and probably earlier
version is in the National Gallery. The
subject derives from *Mark*, vi: 21-28.

REDON, Odilon
French, 1840-1916

The Crucifixion

Signed l.r.: ODILON REDON
Oil on canvas, 46 x 27 cm.
Inv. No. 81.1

Exh. cat., Bordeaux, Galerie des
Beaux-Arts, *Odilon Redon*, 1985, no. 108.

Believed to have been painted in 1904.
The composition is based on the
Crucifixion (c. 1526) by Grünewald in
the Kunsthalle, Karlsruhe.

Follower of
REMBRANDT Harmensz. van Rijn
Dutch, 1606-69

An old warrior

Oil on canvas, 74.7 x 64.6 cm.
Inv. No. 41.7

A false signature, *Rembrandt f. 1651*, was
removed in 1967.

RENOIR, Pierre-Auguste
French, 1841-1919

Young woman seated

Signed l.l.: Renoir
Oil on canvas, 66 x 55.5 cm.
Inv. No. 84.1

F. Daulte, *Auguste Renoir*, I, 1971,
no. 227; exh. cat., London, Arts Council,
Renoir, 1985, no. 43; BMAG 1991,
pp. 20-1.

Painted c. 1876/7, the picture has often
been known since the late 19th century
as *La Pensée* (Thought). The model has
been identified as a professional, Nini
Lopez.

REYNOLDS, Sir Joshua
British, 1723-92

Portrait of a young man

Oil on canvas, 34.3 x 24.1 cm.
Inv. No. 69.10

E. K. Waterhouse, *Reynolds*, 1973,
pp. 15-16; exh. cat., Plymouth City
Museum and Art Gallery, *Sir Joshua
Reynolds*, 1973, no. 7; D. Mannings,
Burl. Mag., CXVII, April 1975, p. 220.

Painted c. 1746.

[REYNOLDS, Sir Joshua]

Portrait of the Rev. William Beele

Oil on canvas, 76.2 x 63.5 cm.
Inv. No. 70.1

E.K. Waterhouse, *Reynolds*, 1973, p. 15;
D. Mannings, *Burl. Mag.*, CXVII, April
1975, p. 221; exh. cat., London, Tate
Gallery, *Manners & morals*, 1987-8,
no. 190.

Painted c. 1748-9. William Beele
(1704-57) was Chaplain to the Dockyard
at Plymouth. Engraved in 1822 by
S.W. Reynolds.

[REYNOLDS, Sir Joshua]

Portrait of Richard Robinson, D.D.

Oil on canvas, 142.3 x 114.5 cm.
Inv. No. 43.9

A.C. Sewter, *Burl. Mag.*, XC, August 1948, pp. 218-20; E.K. Waterhouse, *Reynolds*, 1973, pp. 12, 48, n. to pl. 95; J. Coleman, *Irish arts review yearbook*, 1995, pp. 131-6.

Painted 1779. Richard Robinson (1709-94) became Archbishop of Armagh and Primate of All Ireland in 1765. He was created 1st Baron Rokeby in 1777. This portrait is the replica of one in the Musée des Beaux-Arts, Bordeaux, which was exhibited in the Royal Academy in 1775 (no. 233) and engraved by J. R. Smith the same year. [See Prints, Smith, p. 137].

RICCI, Sebastiano and Marco
Italian, 1659-1734 and 1676-1730

Allegorical tomb of the 1st Duke of Devonshire

Signed l.r.: B.[astiano] M.[arco] RICCI/Faciebant
Inscribed c.r. on plinth: [MANUS] HAEC/[INI]MICA/[TY]RANNIS
Oil on canvas, 217.8 x 138.4 cm.
Inv. No. 58.4

J. Daniels, *Sebastiano Ricci*, 1976, no. 53.

Painted c. 1725 as part of a series of imaginary tombs commissioned from Italian artists by the Irish impresario, Owen McSwiny, and bought with nine others by the 2nd Duke of Richmond for his dining room at Goodwood. The series commemorated 'illustrious Personnages who flourish'd in England' after the Glorious Revolution of 1688. The figures, tomb, and sculpture are by Sebastiano and the rest by Marco. The inscription may be translated as 'This hand is the enemy of tyrants'. A replica, or early copy, lacking the arched top, is in the Victoria and Albert Museum, and a grisaille reduction, probably by D.M. Fratta, is at Chatsworth.

ROBERT, Hubert
French, 1733-1808

A caprice with a hermitage

Signed and dated l.r.: H/ROBERT/1796
Oil on canvas, 80 x 64.8 cm.
Inv. No. 64.4

P. de Nolhac, *Hubert Robert*, 1910,
p. 137.

ROMNEY, George
British, 1734-1802

Portrait of John Smith

Oil on canvas, 127 x 101.6 cm.
Inv. No. 52.4

H. Ward and W. Roberts, *Romney*, II,
1904, p. 146.

Painted in 1782. The sitter (1703-87)
was a wealthy London merchant. Another
version is recorded (location unknown).

ROSSELLI, Cosimo
Italian, 1439-1507

The Adoration of the Child Jesus

Tempera on wood, arched top,
177.8 x 147.3 cm.
Inv. No. 65.7

B. Berenson, *Italian pictures of the
Renaissance: Florentine school*, I, 1963,
p. 191 (then at Northwick Park).

Probably painted in the 1480s. The
figures kneeling with the Virgin are,
clockwise from the front left, a young
Magus, St Benedict, St Jerome, St
Francis and the two other Magi.

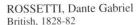

ROSSETTI, Dante Gabriel
British, 1828-82

The blue bower

Signed and dated l.r.: DGR [in monogram]/1865
Oil on canvas, 84 x 70.9 cm.
Inv. No. 59.1

V. Surtees, *The paintings and drawings of Dante Gabriel Rossetti*, I, 1971, no. 178; exh. cat., London, Tate Gallery, *The Pre-Raphaelites*, 1984, no. 132; RA 1998, no. 166.

Exhibited at the Royal Academy in 1883 (no. 303). The sitter was Fanny Cornforth (c. 1826-c. 1906), the artist's model, housekeeper and mistress. Several related drawings are known, including one at Birmingham Museum and Art Gallery.

ROUSSEAU, Pierre-Étienne-Théodore
French, 1812-67

Landscape in the Auvergne

Signed l.l.: TH.R.
Oil on paper, laid on canvas, 33 x 42.2 cm.
Inv. No. 60.12

Exh. cat., Paris, Louvre, *Théodore Rousseau*, 1967-8, no. 5.

Painted in 1830. The location has been identified as near Thiézac, Cantal. A preparatory drawing is in a private collection.

RUBENS, Peter Paul
Flemish, 1577-1640

Portrait of a Carmelite prior

Oil on wood, 79.5 x 65.5 cm.
Inv. No. 99.1

H. Vlieghe, *Corpus Rubenianum, XIX*, 1987, p. 76; M. Jaffé, *Rubens, catalogo completo*, 1989, no. 330.

Acquired with financial assistance from the National Art Collections Fund and the Friends of the Barber Institute.

Probably datable to 1616, when the artist was painting a large altarpiece for the Church of the Calced Carmelites in Brussels.

[RUBENS, Peter Paul]
Landscape in Flanders
Oil on wood, 89.8 x 133.8 cm.
Inv. No. 40.11

W. Adler, *Corpus Rubenianum, XVIII: Landscapes*, I, 1982, no. 59; exh. cat., London, National Gallery, *Making and meaning: Rubens's landscapes*, 1996, no. 46, pp. 63-5, 120.

Later figures, some derived from the artist's *The Park of a Castle* (Kunsthistorisches Museum, Vienna) were removed from the foreground in 1940. Engraved by Schelte Adamsz. Bolswert before 1659. [see Prints, Bolswert, p. 128].

Follower of
RUBENS
Head of a young woman
Oil on wood, 56.5 x 48.8 cm.
Inv. No. 50.1

M. Rooses, *L'oeuvre de P.P. Rubens*, IV, 1890, p. 173; H. Lahrkamp, *Westfalen*, LX(1), 1982, p. 126, no. 80 (as by J. Bockhorst).

The model was named as Helena Fourment, the artist's wife, by Sir Joshua Reynolds, the first known owner. This identification is extremely doubtful, however, as is the attribution to Rubens. The work has been ascribed to Johann Bockhorst (1604-68).

RUISDAEL, Jacob van
Dutch, 1628/9-82
A woodland landscape

Signed l.r.: JvR [in monogram]
Oil on canvas, 61 x 84.5 cm.
Inv. No. 38.11

Exh. cat., Newcastle, Laing Art Gallery, *Dutch landscape painting*, 1983, no. 37.

Possibly painted in the 1650s. The figures and animals are ascribed to Adriaen van de Velde (1636-72). A signed repetition (location now unknown) was on the Lucerne art market in 1969.

SICKERT, Walter Richard
British, 1860-1942

The Eldorado, Paris

Oil on canvas, 48.2 x 59 cm.
Inv. No. 68.3

W. Baron, *Sickert*, 1973, no. 235.

Painted c. 1906. The Eldorado was a *café-concert* on the Boulevard de Strasbourg. An oil sketch is in a British private collection.

SIGNORELLI, Luca
Italian, 1441?-1523

Portrait of Niccolò Vitelli

Inscribed: N.V.
Tempera on wood, 44.2 x 33 cm.
Inv. No. 45.3

Exh. cats., Cortona, Palazzo Pretorio, and Florence, Palazzo Strozzi, *Luca Signorelli*, 1953, no. 19; London, National Gallery, *Signorelli in British collections*, 1998-9, no. 11.

The sitter (1414-86) was ruler of Città di Castello, Umbria, from 1468. Similar portraits of his two sons are in the Villa I Tatti, near Florence.

SIMONE Martini
Italian, c. 1284-1344

St John the Evangelist

Inscribed l.c.: Anno. dñi. M.CCC.XX
Tempera on wood, 41.7 x 30.3 cm., including integral frame
Inv. No. 38.12

A. Martindale, *Simone Martini*, 1988, no. 8; D. Hemsoll, *Apollo*, CXLVII, Feb. 1998, pp. 3-10.

The panel formed the right wing of a composite altarpiece, whose other sections remain unidentified. The verso is decorated in simulation of a leather book-binding.

SOLIMENA, Francesco
Italian, 1657-1747

The Holy Trinity with the Madonna and saints

Oil on canvas, 101 x 128 cm.
Inv. No. 67.6

Exh. cat., London, Heim Gallery, *Baroque sketches, drawings & sculptures*, 1967, no. 15.

The modello for the altarpiece in the Franciscan church of S. Girolamo delle Monache, Naples, which was probably painted c. 1705. On the left, Saints Francis and Clare appear with Franciscan nuns. To the right is the mitred St Benedict, and below the Madonna, St Jerome is seated with his lion.

SPANISH
19th century

Portrait of an old woman

Oil on canvas, 105 x 85 cm.
Inv. No. 40.5

BI 1952, p. 54 (as by Goya).

STEEN, Jan
Dutch, 1625/6-79

The wrath of Ahasuerus

Signed l.l.:J. Steen [JS in monogram]
Oil on canvas, 129 x 167 cm.
Inv. No. 39.22

B.D. Kirschenbaum, *The religious and historical paintings of Jan Steen*, 1977, no. 18; exh. cat., Washington D.C., National Gallery of Art and elsewhere, *Jan Steen, painter and storyteller*, 1996, no. 44.

Painted c. 1671-3. The subject is based on *Esther*, vii: 1-7. Several other versions exist, notably in the Cleveland Museum of Art and a British private collection.

STOM, Matthias
Dutch, c. 1600-?after 1652

Isaac blessing Jacob

Oil on canvas, 136.5 x 182 cm.
Inv. No. 94.2

RA 1998, no. 293; exh. cat., Barber
Institute, *Matthias Stom, 'Isaac blessing
Jacob'*, 1999, no. 1.

Acquired with financial assistance from
the National Art Collections Fund and
the Museums and Galleries Commission/
Victoria and Albert Museum Purchase
Grant Fund.

Painted c. 1635, when Stom was in Italy.
The subject is from *Genesis*, xxvii: 1-29.
The pendant, *Christ among the Doctors*,
is in an American private collection.

STROZZI, Bernardo
Italian, 1581-1644

Head of an old woman

Oil on canvas, 48.3 x 38.8 cm.
Inv. No. 66.8

L. Mortari, *Bernardo Strozzi*, 1966,
p. 177 (then in the Böström collection).

TENIERS, David the younger
Flemish, 1610-90

The bleaching ground

Signed l.r.: DAVID TENIERS F
Oil on canvas, 85 x 120.5 cm.
Inv. No. 47.1

J. Smith, *A catalogue raisonné of [...]
Dutch and Flemish painters*, III, 1831,
p. 396, no. 511; exh. cat., Antwerp,
Koninklijk Museum voor Schone Kunsten,
David Teniers the younger, 1991, no. 27.

Painted in the mid-1640s. A smaller
version, lacking the church is in the
Gemäldegalerie, Dresden. The theme is
the spring wash and bleaching after the
winter. The site is unidentified.

TIBERIO d'Assisi
Italian, c. 1470-1524

St Ansanus

Fresco, transferred to canvas,
153 x 70 cm.
Inv. No. 44.4a

BI 1952, pp. 106-9; B. Berenson, *Italian pictures of the Renaissance: Central Italian and North Italian schools*, I, 1968, p. 427.

Ansanus (died 303), first patron saint of Siena, is holding human lungs and liver. This fragment, together with nos. 44.4b and 44.4c, and others representing the Madonna and Child and St Sebastian (both unlocated), were in the church at Bastia, near Assisi, in 1872. By then they had already been transferred to canvas.

[TIBERIO d'Assisi]

St Clare

Fresco, transferred to canvas,
153 x 70 cm.
Inv. No. 44.4b

For literature and comment, see above, no. 44.4a.

St Clare (c. 1194-1253) was a follower of St Francis, and founder of the Order of Poor Clares.

[TIBERIO d'Assisi]

St Francis of Assisi

Fresco, transferred to canvas,
153 x 70 cm.
Inv. No. 44.4c

For literature and comment, see above, no. 44.4a.

TINTORETTO, Jacopo Robusti, called
Italian, 1518-94

Portrait of a young man

Inscribed u.r.: ANNO 1554 MENSE MA/AETATIS SUAE 22
Oil on canvas, 121 x 93.3 cm.
Inv. No. 37.13

P. Rossi, *Jacopo Tintoretto*, I, 1974, pp. 38, 99.

The inscription records that the portrait was painted 'in the year 1554, in the month of May [or March], in the 22nd year of his age'.

TOULOUSE-LAUTREC, Henri de
French, 1864-1901

A woman seated in a garden

Signed l.l. and l.r.: HTLautrec [the initials in monogram]
Oil on cardboard, 49.4 x 31.3 cm.
Inv. No. 48.6

M.G. Dortu, *Toulouse-Lautrec et son oeuvre*, II, 1971, no. 366; BMAG 1991, p. 46.

Painting in 1890 in the garden of Père Forest in Montmartre. The unidentified sitter appears in other works by Lautrec between 1889 and 1891.

TROY, Jean-François de
French, 1679-1752

Jason taming the bulls of Aeëtes

Oil on canvas, 55.3 x 128.9 cm.
Inv. No. 61.1

G. Brière, in L. Dimier, ed., *Les Peintres français du XVIIIe siècle*, II, 1930, pp. 26-7, 37, no. 54.

The source of the subject is Ovid, *Metamorphoses*, vii: 110-21. Executed in 1742, this is a sketch for the painting in the Musée Crozatier, Le Puy, of 1744. The latter is itself a design for one of seven tapestries illustrating the story of Jason. A set of these tapestries is in the Victoria and Albert Museum, and two other sketches are in the National Gallery.

TURNER, Joseph Mallord William
British, 1775-1851

The sun rising through vapour

Signed l.r.: J.M.W. Turner R A
Oil on canvas, 69.2 x 101.6 cm.
Inv. No. 38.1

M. Butlin and E. Joll, *The paintings of J.M.W. Turner*, 1977, no. 95.

Painted c. 1809. A pencil study for the picture is on p. 70 of Turner's 'Spithead' sketchbook in the British Museum. A slightly earlier picture of a similar theme is in the National Gallery.

UGOLINO di Nerio
Italian, active 1317-27

St Francis of Assisi

Tempera on wood, pointed top,
88.2 x 32.2 cm.
Inv. No. 43.6

B. Berenson, *Italian pictures of the Renaissance: Central Italian and North Italian schools*, I, 1968, p. 437; J. H. Stubblebine, *Duccio di Buoninsegna and his school*, I, 1979, pp. 182, 183 (as by the 'Clark Polyptych Master').

Part of a composite altarpiece, now lost. The sides and base of the frame are modern, but the angel above seems contemporary with the main figure.

VERONESE, Paolo Caliari, called
Italian, 1528-88

The Visitation

Oil on canvas, 277.5 x 156 cm.
Inv. No. 53.5

T. Pignatti, *Veronese*, I, 1976, no. A21.

The subject is taken from *Luke*, i: 39 ff. Originally in the church of S. Giacomo, Murano, the painting was engraved by V. Le Febvre in 1682 [See Prints, p. 133]. A sheet of experimental studies for the composition was formerly in the Museum Boymans-van Beuningen, Rotterdam.

VIGÉE-LEBRUN, Élisabeth Louise
French, 1755-1842

Portrait of Countess Golovine

Oil on canvas, the corners sloped,
83.5 x 66.7 cm.
Inv. No. 80.1

Exh. cat., Fort Worth, Kimbell Art
Museum, *Elisabeth Louise Vigée-Lebrun
1755-1842*, 1982, no. 46; RA 1998,
no. 332.

Probably painted in Moscow between
1797 and 1800. The sitter was Varvara
Nikolaevna Golovine, née Galitzine
(1766-1821).

VLIET, Hendrick Cornelisz. van der
Dutch, 1611/2-75

A grotto in an imaginary landscape

Signed and dated l.r.: H Vandervliet
164[3?]
Oil on wood, 54.7 x 90.2 cm.
Inv. No. 66.1

VUILLARD, Édouard
French, 1868-1940

Madame Vuillard arranging her hair

Signed l.l.: E Vuillard
Oil on millboard, 49.5 x 35.5 cm.
Inv. No. 63.3

B. Thomson, *Vuillard*, 1988, pp. 10-11;
exh. cat., Glasgow, Art Gallery and
Museum and elsewhere, *Vuillard*, 1991,
pp. 22, 27, 29 and no. 60; BMAG 1991,
p. 55.

Painted in 1900 in the apartment which
the artist shared with his mother in the
rue Truffaut, Paris. He painted her
frequently until her death in 1928.

Ascribed to
WATTEAU, Jean-Antoine
French, 1684-1721

A man playing a hurdy-gurdy

Oil on canvas, 22.7 x 18 cm.
Inv. No. 56.9

G. Macchia and E.C. Montagni, *Watteau*, 1968, p. 128, 8-G.

Possibly painted by Watteau's follower, Nicolas Lancret (1690-1743).

WHISTLER, James McNeill
British, 1834-1903

Symphony in White, No. III

Inscribed, signed and dated l.l.:
Symphony in White, No. III.-Whistler.
1867- [the figure 7 written over a 5]
Oil on canvas, 51.4 x 76.9 cm.
Inv. No. 39.24

A. McL. Young and others, *The paintings of James McNeill Whistler*, 1980, no. 61; exh. cat., London, Tate Gallery and elsewhere, *James McNeill Whistler*, 1994, no. 16.

Begun in 1865 and completed and exhibited at the Royal Academy in 1867 (no. 233). It was the first picture to be shown by Whistler under a musical title - an innovation which led to a celebrated controversy between the artist and the critic, P.G. Hamerton. The models were Joanna Hiffernan, Whistler's mistress (left), and Milly Jones. Related drawings are in the Munson-Williams-Proctor Institute, Utica, N.Y., and the Hunterian Art Gallery, Glasgow.

WILSON, Richard
British, 1714-82

The River Dee, near Eaton Hall

Signed l.r.: R W
Oil on canvas, 54 x 88.6 cm.
Inv. No. 37.11

W.G. Constable, *Richard Wilson*, 1953, pp. 173-5, n. to pl. 34; exh. cat., London, Tate Gallery, *Richard Wilson*, 1983, no. 83.

The prime version of a view frequently repeated, with variations, by the artist, this was painted c. 1759-60. It is taken about 6 miles south of Chester, with the hills of Wales in the background. A related drawing is in the Art Institute of Chicago. Engraved, with additional figures, by T. Morris, 1774. [See Prints, Morris, p. 134].

WITTE, Emanuel de
Dutch, 1615/7-91/2

Interior of the Oude Kerk, Amsterdam

Signed l.r.: E. De Witte Ao 1 [final figures illegible]
Oil on canvas, 83.5 x 66.5 cm.
Inv. No. 74.2

I. Manke, *Emanuel de Witte*, 1963, no. 45.

The artist painted over 40 views of the interior of the Oude Kerk (St Nicholas), including a number from this viewpoint, notably that in the Statens Museum for Kunst, Copenhagen. The present picture is probably a late work.

Studio of
ZURBARÁN, Francisco de
Spanish, 1598-1664

St Marina

Inscribed u.r.: STA. MARINA
Oil on canvas, 160 x 107 cm.
Inv. No. 52.1

One of a number of later workshop
variants on Zurbarán's *St Margaret* in the
National Gallery. St. Marina, or Margaret,
of Antioch died in the early 4th century.
She is depicted as a shepherdess, with
crook and saddlebags.

DRAWINGS & WATERCOLOURS

(recto)

(detail of verso)

BARTOLOMMEO, Fra
Italian, 1472-1517

The Madonna and Child with saints
(recto)

Two figures (verso)

Black and yellow chalk heightened with white on tinted paper, 260 x 196 mm.
Inv. No. 36.1

H. von der Gabelentz, *Fra Bartolommeo und die Florentiner Renaissance*, I, 1922, p. 150, and II, no. 304; MM 1986, no. 3; exh. cat., Nottingham University Art Gallery and elsewhere, *Drawing in the Italian Renaissance workshop*, 1983, no. 63.

A study for the altarpiece in the church of S. Marco, Florence, painted by Fra Bartolommeo in 1509 (now in the Uffizi). Other drawings are in the Uffizi, the Museum Boymans-van Beuningen, Rotterdam, the Courtauld Institute, and elsewhere.

(recto)

(verso)

[BARTOLOMMEO, Fra]

An Italian hill town (recto)

A farm among trees (verso)

Pen, brown and black ink,
288 x 217 mm.
Inv. No. 57.14

MM 1986, no. 4

The landscape has not been identified.

BEARDSLEY, Aubrey
British, 1872-98

The Battle of the Beaux and the Belles

Inscribed on verso: Leonard Smithers
Esq.,/Effingham House/Arundel Street,/
Strand S W C/London/same size as
others/879
Pen and black ink, 257 x 176 mm.
Inv. No. 52.5

B. Reade, *Beardsley*, 1967, p. 353, n. 411;
S. Wilson, *Beardsley*, 1983, p. 23 and
no. 32; MM 1986, no. 34.

A drawing for the eighth illustration to
Alexander Pope's *Rape of the Lock*
(canto v) in the edition published by
Leonard Smithers in May 1896.

CORTONA, Pietro Berretini da
Italian, 1596-1669

A wooded river landscape

Black chalk, brush and grey ink, grey wash, 283 x 425 mm.
Inv. No. 92.2

Bought jointly with Birmingham Museums and Art Gallery, with financial assistance from the National Art Collections Fund and National Heritage Memorial Fund.

G. Briganti, *Pietro da Cortona o della pittura barocca*, 1982, p. 290; A.E. Popham and C. Lloyd, *Old Master drawings at Holkham Hall*, 1986, no. 105; RA 1998, no. 94.

Probably datable c. 1650.

DEGAS, Hilaire-Germain-Edgar
French, 1834-1917

Mademoiselle Malo

Signed l.l.: Degas
Pastel on buff paper, 522 x 411 mm.
Inv. No. 49.12

P.-A. Lemoisne, *Degas et son oeuvre*, II, 1946, no. 444; MM 1986, no. 30: BMAG 1991, pp. 24-5.

Datable c. 1875. The sitter is believed to have been a dancer at the Paris Opéra. An oil-sketch, probably of the same sitter, is in the Detroit Institute of Arts, and a larger portrait in oil, for which the present work may be a study, is in the National Gallery of Art, Washington, D.C.

[DEGAS, Hilaire-Germain-Edgar]

Miss La La at the Cirque Fernando

Inscribed and dated u.l.: Miss La La/
25 Janv. 79
Sale stamp l.l.: Degas
Black chalk with touches of pastel,
470 x 320 mm.
Inv. No. 36.7

D. Sutton, *Edgar Degas, life and work*,
1986, p. 130; MM 1986, no. 31; BMAG
1991, p. 26.

The final working drawing, squared for
transfer, for the figure in the painting *La
La at the Cirque Fernando* (1879) in the
National Gallery. The subject was a
mulatto acrobat, noted for the strength of
her teeth and jaws. In addition to three
fleeting notebook sketches, seven other
studies for the figure are known, including
two pastels, in the Tate Gallery and the
J.B. Speed Art Museum, Louisville.

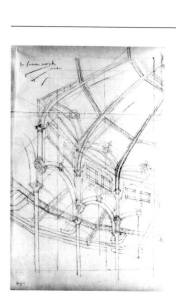

[DEGAS, Hilaire-Germain-Edgar]

*The Cirque Fernando – architectural
study*

Inscribed u.l.: les fermes sont plus penchés
Sale stamp l.l.: Degas
Black and red chalk and pencil on two
sheets of joined pink paper, 480 x 313 mm.
Inv. No. 38.10

D. Sutton, *Edgar Degas, life and work*,
1986, p. 130; MM 1986, no. 32; BMAG
1991, p. 27.

A study for the architectural background
of *La La at the Cirque Fernando* (see
previous entry). The Cirque Fernando
was built in 1875 in the boulevard
Rochechouart, Paris, near the place
Pigalle. Studies for the interior fill
several pages of one of the artist's
notebooks. The inscription states that
'the rafters are more slanting'.

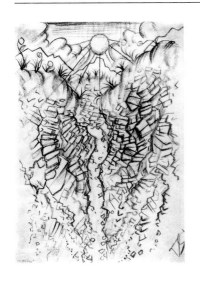

DIX, Otto
German, 1891-1969

Chalk cliffs in the sun

Signed l.r.: DI
Black chalk on beige paper, 284 x 208 mm.
Inv. No. 92.5

Datable to 1916 and apparently from a
sketchbook compiled during the artist's
service in the German field artillery
during the First World War.

DOOMER, Lambert
Dutch, c. 1622/3-1700

Rock dwellings at Saumur on the Loire

Inscribed, signed and dated on verso:
Omtrent Sameurs aen de rivier de
Loore/Doomer f. Ao 1646
Pen with grey and brown washes,
228 x 365 mm.
Inv. No. 37.8

W. Schulz, *Lambert Doomer. Sämtliche
Zeichnungen*, 1974, no. 110; MM 1986,
no. 20.

One of a number of drawings made in
the Loire Valley by the artist en route for
Holland from Nantes in 1646. Others
showing the rock dwellings at Saumur
are in the Kupferstichkabinett, Berlin, the
Städelsches Kunstinstitut, Frankfurt, the
Hermitage, St Petersburg, and two
private collections.

DU MAURIER, George
British, 1834-96

The Triumph of Realism

Signed l.c.: du Maurier
Caption below image: Triumph of
Realism. Blenkinsop (complacently
gazing at a bust of himself by a
fashionable sculptor): 'It's not so much
as a work of art that I value it, Brown!
but the *likeness* is so wonderful you
know!'
Pen, brown ink and pencil; sheet size,
254 x 358 mm.
Inv. No. 52.3

L. Ormond, *George du Maurier*, 1969,
pp. 383-5; MM 1986, no. 33.

Drawn for a cartoon in *Punch*, 17 May
1879, p. 226. The image occupies the left
side of the paper; to the right and above
are the remains of working drawings,
written instructions, wording for the
caption and date of publication. The
busts depict from left, Thomas Reynolds
Lamont (1826-98), Thomas Armstrong
(1835-1911), and Du Maurier himself.

DÜRER, Albrecht
German, 1471-1528

A man with an oar

Inscribed u.r.: AD [in monogram]
Pen and brown ink, 160 x 104 mm.
Inv. No. 54.9

E. Panofsky, *Albrecht Dürer*, I. 1945,
p. 216 and II, 1945, no. 1261;
MM 1986, no. 2.

One of a number of sheets believed to
have come from a sketchbook made by
Dürer on his journey to the Netherlands
c. 1520-1.

DUTCH (?)
17th century

Landscape

Pen and brown wash, 246 x 146 mm.
Inv. No. 36.2

M. Röthlisberger, *Claude Lorrain, the paintings*, I, 1961, pp. 144-5.

Possibly by a Dutch imitator of Claude, working in Italy. The subject has some affinities with the centre of no. 24 in Claude's *Liber Veritatis* in the British Museum.

DYCK, Anthony van
Flemish, 1599-1641

An English landscape

Watercolour and bodycolour with pen, 189 x 267 mm.
Inv. No. 39.20

MM 1986, no. 11; RA 1998, no. 98; exh. cat., London, British Museum, and elsewhere, *The light of nature*, 1999, no. 24.

The location is unidentified, but perhaps Rye or Greenwich. One of a small group of watercolours of extensive landscapes executed by van Dyck in England between 1635 and 1641. Others are in the British Museum, the J. Paul Getty Museum, Los Angeles, and at Chatsworth.

FERRARI, Gaudenzio (?)
Italian, c. 1475-1546

The Madonna and Child with St Mary Magdalene and a bishop

Black chalk on joined sheets of grey paper, mounted on vellum, 833 x 900 mm.
Inv. No. 48.7

C. Gould, *National Gallery catalogues: sixteenth century schools*, 1975, p. 128; exh. cat., Turin, Accademia Albertina, *Gaudenzio Ferrari e la sua scuola*, 1982, p. 161; MM 1986, no. 5.

Closely related to the painting by Gaudenzio's pupil, Bernardino Lanino, *The Madonna and Child with saints*, dated 1543, in the National Gallery.

GAINSBOROUGH, Thomas
British, 1727-88

A hilly landscape

Black chalk and stump and white chalk on blue paper, 271 x 335 mm.
Inv. No. 37.4

J. Hayes, *The drawings of Thomas Gainsborough*, I, 1970, no. 386; MM 1986, no. 24.

Probably executed c. 1775-80. There is a slightly smaller version in the Seattle Art Museum.

GOYEN, Jan van
Dutch, 1596-1656

A village scene

Signed and dated l.r.: V G 1631
Black chalk, pen and grey wash, 111 x 186 mm.
Inv. No. 36.8

H.-U. Beck, *Jan van Goyen*, I, 1972, no. 99; MM 1986, no. 10.

Another drawing by van Goyen of the same subject and date is in the Albertina, Vienna.

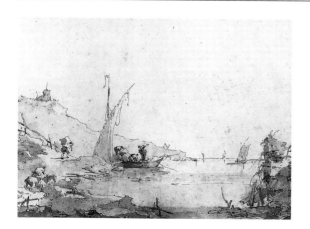

GUARDI, Francesco
Italian, 1712-93

A coastal scene

Pen and brown wash with traces of black chalk, 251 x 369 mm.
Inv. No. 36.3

Exh. cat., Venice, Fondazione Cini, *Canaletto e Guardi*, 1962, no. 78; MM 1986, no. 23.

Datable c. 1770-80. On the mount are the collectors' marks of William Esdaile (Lugt 2617) and J.P. Heseltine (Lugt 1507). A repetition, probably a late copy, is in the British Museum.

HOLBEIN, Hans the younger
Swiss, 1497/8-1543

Design for a glass painting

Inscribed l.c.: H Holbein [the letters H joined]
Collectors' marks: Sir Peter Lely (Lugt 1753, twice); Jonathan Richardson senior (Lugt 2184).
Pen and grey wash with traces of black chalk, 375 x 295 mm.
Inv. No. 55.20

MM 1986, no. 6; exh. cat., London, British Museum, *The age of Dürer and Holbein*, 1988, no. 192.

Executed c. 1520. A companion design is in the Albertina, Vienna.

HOLLAR Wenceslaus
Bohemian, 1607-77

The Thames below Westminster Pier

Signed l.r.: W. Hollar. D.
Inscribed in the sky: Lambeth house/ Parliament house/Westminster Hall
Pen and brown ink, 146 x 401 mm.
Inv. No. 54.3

Exh. cat., Manchester City Art Gallery, *Wenceslaus Hollar*, 1963, no. D 75; MM 1986, no. 16.

Related to a drawing dated 1638, sold at Sotheby's with the Springell collection, 30 June 1986 (no. 22). Hollar also made an etching of the same prospect from a little further up the river.

INGRES, Jean-Auguste-Dominique
French, 1780-1867

'La belle Ferronnière'

Inscribed l.l.: [D]essiné par Ingres élève de/son cher maître David
Black chalk, stump and wash, 525 x 418 mm.
Inv. No. 37.3

Exh. cats., MM 1986, no. 28; Paris, Louvre, *Copier/créer. De Turner à Picasso*, 1993, no. 180, pp. 276-7.

A copy after the painting in the Louvre often attributed to Leonardo da Vinci and previously thought to represent 'la belle Ferronnière', mistress of Francis I. Datable c. 1802-6. A smaller version is in the Musée Ingres, Montauban.

The Aga Khan

Vera Canning

Noel Coward

KAPP, Edmond Xavier
British, 1890-1978

243 portrait and caricature drawings

Signed and dated as indicated
Pen, wash, chalk, charcoal etc., mainly on paper, of various sizes between 572 x 435 and 82 x 106 mm.
Inv Nos. 69.9/1-241 and 71.2/1-2

The subjects are:
Richard Adeney, flautist, 1935; The Aga Khan, League of Nations, 1935 (illustrated); Henry Ainsley, actor, 1932; Baron Aloÿsi, League of Nations, 1934; Sir Norman Angell, author, 1914; Ernest Ansermet, conductor, 1920; Michael Arlen, novelist, 1921; Sholem Asch, author, 1930; Joseph Avenol, League of Nations, 1933; Sir Horace Avory, judge, 1931; Harley Granville Barker, playwright, 1913; Dr Ernest Barnes, Bishop of Birmingham, 1930; Louis Barthou, League of Nations, 1934; Sir Thomas Beecham, conductor, 1919/1930/1937/1948 (two); Sir Max Beerbohm, caricaturist, 1923; President Beneš of Czechoslovakia, League of Nations, 1935; Arnold Bennett, author, 1929; Henry Bérenger, League of Nations, 1934; Desmond Bernal, scientist, 1927; Laurence Binyon, poet, 1921; Lord Birkenhead, politician, 1914 (two); Augustine Birrell, writer, 1913; Léon Blum, politician, 1947; Arthur Bodansky, conductor, 1914; Horatio Bottomley, financier, 1928; Sir Adrian Boult, conductor, 1932/1943; Dr Frank Buchman, League of Nations, 1935; Lord Buckmaster, Lord Chancellor, 1929; Davy Burnaby, comedian, 1919; Ferruccio Busoni, musician, 1921; Basil Cameron, conductor, 1943; Vera Canning, cellist, 1938 (illustrated); Pablo Casals, cellist, 1950 (two)/1950-9/1958; René Cassin, lawyer, 1946; Viscount Cecil, League of Nations, 1935/1936; Fedor Chaliapin, singer, 1928; The Earl of Chesterfield, courtier, 1914; G.K. Chesterton, writer, 1932; Richard Church, writer, 1957; Sir Winston Churchill, statesman, 1929; Willie Clarkson, wig-maker, 1929, Dr John Clifford, President, Baptist World Alliance, 1913; Harriet Cohen, pianist, 1930/1938; John Collier, author, 1930/1931; Mrs Margery Corbett-Ashby, League of Nations, 1934; Alfred Cortot, pianist, 1928; Noel Coward, entertainer 1930 (illustrated); Edric Cundell, conductor, 1944; Robert Cunninghame-Graham, writer, 1919; Malcolm Davis, League of Nations, 1933; Frederick Delius, composer, 1932; Dr Engelbert Dollfuss, League of Nations, 1933; Arnold Dolmetsch, musician, 1921; Sir Gerald du Maurier, actor-manager, 1928; Anthony Eden, League of Nations, 1935; Albert Einstein, physicist, 1931; Sir Edward Elgar, musician, 1914 (two); T.S. Eliot, poet, 1919; Adila Fachiri, violinist, 1930; Sydney Fairbrother, comédienne, 1919; Anatole Fistoulari, conductor, 1942/1943; E.M. Forster, author, 1930; King George VI, 1932; Dr Joseph Goebbels, League of Nations, 1935; Walter Goehr, conductor, 1942/1943; Louis Golding, writer, 1930; Sir Eugene

Goosens, conductor, 1932; Richard Goulden, actor, 1927; George Graves, comedian, 1919; John Grierson, film-producer, 1946; George Grossman, comedian, 1919; Sacha Guitry, entertainer, 1946; Dr Norman Haire, gynaecologist, 1929; Cicely Hamilton, writer, 1931 (two); Ida Händel, violinist, 1943; Beatrice Harrison, cellist, 1928; Arthur Henderson, League of Nations, 1935; Leslie Henson, comedian, 1930; Myra Hess, pianist, 1931; Frederick Higgins, poet, 1914; Sir Samuel Hoare, League of Nations, 1934/1935; Gustav Holst, composer, 1924; Sir Frederick Hopkins, bio-chemist, 1943; Lord Howard de Walden, librettist, 1922; Aldous Huxley, author, 1924; Sir Julian Huxley, biologist, 1947 (two); Paul Hymans, League of Nations, 1934; Henry Hyndham, socialist, 1914; William Inge, Dean of St Paul's, 1930; Earl Jellicoe, admiral, 1928; Augustus John, artist, 1920; Léon Jouhaux, League of Nations, 1935; Sir William Joynson-Hicks, politician, 1928; Buster Keaton, comedian, 1935; Rudyard Kipling, author, 1914; Fritz Kreisler, violinist, 1914 (two); Constant Lambert, composer, 1931; Wanda Landowska, pianist, 1930; George Lansbury, politician, 1929 (two); Pierre Laval, League of Nations, 1934; D. H. Lawrence, author, 1923; Stephen Leacock, humorist, 1920; Lotte Lehmann, singer, 1928; Jenö Léner, violinist, 1930; Stanley Lief, National Healing pioneer, 1936; Maxim Litvinoff, League of Nations, 1934/1935; Sir Oliver Lodge, scientist, first Principal of Birmingham University, 1919/1931; Dr Lu Gwei Djen, academic, 1965; Salvador de Madariaga, League of Nations, 1934 (two); Thomas Mann, author, 1931/1932; Guglielmo Marconi, pioneer of wireless, 1932; Filippo Marinetti, poet, 1921; Lord Marks, businessman, c. 1930; Kingsley Martin, journalist, 1936; John Masefield, poet, 1917; Charles Masterman, politician, 1914; Sir John Maude, civil servant, 1946; James Maxton, politician, 1930; Lord Melchett, industrialist, 1929; Yehudi Menuhin, violinist, 1957; Corneille Mertens, League of Nations, 1935; Viscount Milner, politician, 1914; Benno Moiseiwitsch, pianist, undated; George Moore, novelist, 1933; Viscount Morley, politician, 1914; Sir Oswald Mosley, politician, 1939; Sir Neville Mott, physicist, 1966 (two) Frank Mullingo, singer, 1919; Gilbert Murray, academic, 1928; Dr Castillo Najera, League of Nations, 1934; Joseph Needham, academic, 1946; Sir Henry Newbolt, writer, 1913; Max Nordan, writer, 1914; Sian O'Kelly, President of Eire, 1935; The Earl of Onslow, politician, 1917; Vladimir Pachmann, pianist, 1911; Ignace Paderewski, pianist, 1923; Isabel de Palencia, League of Nations, 1934; Joseph Paul-Boncour, League of Nations, 1934; Dr Max Planck, physicist, 1932 (two); Sir Nigel Playfair, actor, 1927; Lord Plumer, field-marshal, 1919; J.B. Priestley, author, 1947; Maurice Ravel, composer, 1923; Lord Reading, Viceroy of India, 1929; Lord Reith, Director-General of the BBC,

1931; Franz Reizenstein, pianist, 1944; Primo de Rivera, Regent of Spain, 1926; George Robey, actor, 1932; Theodore Roosevelt, President of the U.S.A., 1914; Lord Rothschild, zoologist, 1930; Walter Runciman, politician, 1929; Dora Russell, writer, 1929; George Russell ["A.E."], poet, 1919; Harold Samuel, pianist, 1930/1932; Lord Samuel, politician, 1929; Sir John Sargent, educationalist, 1946; Sir Malcolm Sargent, conductor, 1930/1946; Arthur Schnabel, pianist, 1932; Arnold Schönberg, composer, 1931; Elisabeth Schumann, singer, 1930; Charles Scott, journalist, 1931; Andres Segovia, guitarist, 1929/1955/1958; Gordon Selfridge, businessman, 1928; George Bernard Shaw, writer, 1930; Abbey Simon, pianist, 1957; Logan Pearsall Smith, writer, 1922; Solomon [Solomon Cutner], pianist, 1940; Stephen Spender, poet, 1946; Sir Charles Villiers Stanford, composer, 1913; Dr Heathcote Statham, organist, 1943; James Stephens, poet, 1931; G.B. Stern, novelist, 1930; Isaac Stern, violinist, 1951; Dr Marie Stopes, pioneer of birth control, 1929; Lytton Strachey, author, 1929; Richard Strauss, composer, 1915/1931 (two); Rabindranath Tagore, writer, 1921 (two); Jacques Tati, film-actor, 1958; Lionel Tertis, violist, 1933; Sybil Thorndike, actress, 1926; Violet Vanbrugh, actress 1919; Dr Augusto de Vasconcelos, League of Nations 1934; Ralph Vaughan Williams, composer; 1915; Professor Arthur Verrall, academic, 1911; Edgar Wallace, writer, 1931/1932; Sir Hugh Walpole, novelist, 1940 (two); H.G. Wells, author, 1921/1930; Ellen Wilkinson, politician, 1930; Sir Henry Wood, conductor, 1929/1942/1943 (two)/ 1944; W.B. Yeats, poet, 1914; Israel Zangwill, writer, 1924.

GROUPS:
Sir Thomas Beecham with orchestra, 1958 (two); Pablo Casals with ensemble, 1950/1950-9; Pablo Casals, Joseph Szigeti, violinist and John Wummer, flautist, 1951; The Jubilee Singers, 1954 (two); Mr and Mrs Raphael Kubelik, musicians, 1956; Jean Pougnet, violinist, with orchestra, 1943; Sir Henry Wood with audience, 1938; Sir Henry Wood with orchestra, 1930/1942.

KEENE, Charles Samuel
British, 1823-91

The coal famine

Signed l.l.: C K [in monogram]
Inscribed on verso: 55, Baker Street
Pen and brown ink, 168 x 114 mm.
Inv. No. 40.4

A variant is also in the Barber Institute;
see next entry, no. 15.

Out of place

[KEENE, Charles Samuel]

*The Life and Letters of C.S. Keene:
Original Drawings*

A volume containing 24 mounted pen
drawings, some signed, most with
Keene's captions. Sight sizes between
113 x 182 mm. and 144 x 105 mm.
Inv. No. 44.10 (1-24)

1. Untitled
2. *Our auxiliaries*
3. }
4. } *Our reserves*
5. }
6. } *A poser*
7. *Outbreak of humanity*
8. *Music without charms*
9. *A pleasant prospect*
10. *Getting his answer*
11. }
12. } *Home exercise*
13. *Out of place (illustrated)*
14. *A degenerate son*
15. *The coal famine*
16. *Adjustment*
17. *Hibernian veracity*
18. }
19. } *Five o'clock tea*
20. }
21. } *Whose fault?*
22. }
23. } Untitled
24. }

A number of the drawings were reproduced
in *Punch* between 1 February 1868 and
2 January 1875. The volume is bound
uniformly with G.S. Layard, *The Life and
Letters of Charles Samuel Keene*, London,
1892, limited edition de luxe, signed by
the author and numbered 50.

LE BRUN, Charles
French, 1619-90

Portrait head of King Louis XIV

Inscribed indistinctly l.l.
Inscribed on verso: Mr Le Brun. Portrait
de Louis 14e au sortir de sa Maladie
de fièvre ou sa Majesté courut grand
risque. No. 24.
Black, red and white chalk, 435 x 351 mm.
Inv. No. 70.4

F. Stein, *Charles Le Brun: La tenture de
L'Histoire du Roy*, 1985, p. 223; MM
1986, no. 18; exh cat., London, Dulwich
Picture Gallery, *Courage and cruelty.
Le Brun's Horatius Cocles and The
Massacre of the Innocents*, 1990, no. 31.

Le Brun's earliest known portrait of
Louis XIV (1638-1715), drawn c. 1663.
This study was probably used for the
head of the king in *L'Audience du Légat*,
one of a series of Gobelins tapestries
entitled *L'Histoire du Roy*. There are
three later pastels of the king's head and
shoulders in the Louvre.

LEECH, John
British, 1817-64

*Mr Briggs contemplating a day's
fishing*

Signed l.l.: J. Leech
Inscribed below image: Mr Briggs
contemplating a day's fishing, gets his
tackle in order and tries the management
of his running line.
Pen and watercolour over pencil,
240 x 299 mm.
Inv. No. 44.8

S. Houfe, *John Leech and the Victorian
scene*, 1984, p. 226.

A slightly different version was
published in *Punch*, XIX, 1850, p. 78,
and another version was reproduced in
colour and published by Bradbury &
Evans. [See Prints, p. 133].

[LEECH, John]

A bracing day at the seaside

Signed l.l.: J.L.
Watercolour over pencil, 252 x 350 mm.
Inv. No. 44.9

S. Houfe, *John Leech and the Victorian scene*, 1984, p. 164.

The scene takes place at Scarborough. Engraved on wood by Joseph Swain and published in *Mr Punch's Almanack* for 1856. An oil-sketch with variations was exhibited at the Egyptian Hall, London, in 1862.

Attributed to
MAES, Nicolaes
Dutch, 1634-93

Elijah and the Widow of Zarephath

Inscribed l.r.: No. 30
Pen and brown wash, 205 x 325 mm.
Inv. No. 37.9

W. Sumowski, *Drawings of the Rembrandt school*, VIII, 1984, no. 1926; MM 1986, no. 19 (as Jan Victors [?]).

The subject is from I *Kings*, xvii: 10. One of a stylistically coherent group of Rembrandtesque ink drawings formerly ascribed to Jan Victors (1620-76).

MARATTI, Carlo
Italian, 1625-1713

Study for the head of St Charles Borromeo

Red chalk heightened with white on blue paper, 361 x 279 mm.
Inv. No. 37.7

MM 1986, no. 21.

A study for the high altarpiece of the church of Saints Ambrogio e Carlo al Corso, Rome, *St Charles Borromeo presented to Christ by the Virgin, with St Ambrose and an angel* (1685-90). A drawing for this composition is in the Louvre.

Eighth Labour, Driving Tandem

MAY, Philip William (Phil)
British, 1864-1903

The Twelve Labours of 'Arry

15 drawings in 12 mounts, most drawings
signed and dated: Phil May 95
Pen over traces of pencil on card,
various sizes between 330 x 420 mm.
and 190 x 145 mm.
Inv. Nos. 38.8 (1-12)

1. *First Labour, 'Arry skates*
2a-b. *Second Labour, 'Arry plays Billiards*
    (4 drawings on two sheets)
3. *Third Labour, 'Arry catches a Crab*
4. *Fourth Labour, 'Arry plays Cricket*
5. *Fifth Labour, 'Arry at Golf*
    (4 drawings on one sheet)
6. *Sixth Labour, Fishing*
7. *Seventh Labour, 'Arry bikes*
8. *Eighth Labour, Driving Tandem*
    (illustrated)
9a-c. *Ninth Labour, Boxing*
    (3 drawings in one mount)
10. *Tenth Labour, Shooting*
11. *Eleventh Labour, Hunting*
12. *Twelfth Labour, Under the Mistletoe*

J. Thorpe, *English illustration in the
nineties*, 1935, pp. 24-5.

Each mount is inscribed with a title by
the artist. The series was published in
Mr Punch's Almanack for 1896.

[MAY, Philip William (Phil)]

Donkey and cart

Signed and dated l.r.: PHIL MAY 93
Pencil, 181 x 305 mm.
Inv. No. 46.4

[MAY, Philip William (Phil)]
Johnny Toole

Signed l.r.: PHIL
Pen with traces of pencil on card,
110 x 61 mm.
Inv. No. 46.5

May drew J.L. Toole (1830-1906),
a popular comic actor, several times.

METZ, Conrad Martin
German, 1749-1827

The death of the children of Niobe

Signed and dated l.r.: C.M. Metz/Roma
1820
Pen and brown ink and wash, heightened
with white, 454 x 684 mm.
Inv. No. 91.2

Exh. cat., New York, Colnaghi Ltd,
Master drawings, 1990, no. 47.

The subject is taken from Ovid,
Metamorphoses, vi: 204-312.

After
MILLET, Jean-François
French, 1814-75

The drinking place in the forest

Inscribed l.r.: J.F. Millet
Black chalk, 256 x 354 mm.
Inv. No. 37.1

Apparently a copy of the autograph
drawing of the same subject in the
Musée des Beaux-Arts, Lille, which
was executed c. 1856-7.

Ascribed to
NOVELLI, Pietro Antonio
Italian, 1729-1804

A music party

Pen and brown wash over black chalk,
250 x 373 mm.
Inv. No. 38.5

Exh. cat., Venice, Fondazione Cini,
Disegni veneti di collezioni inglesi, 1980,
no. 124; MM 1986, no. 25.

Probably dates from c. 1750. Previously
attributed to P. or A. Longhi, or G.B.
Bison.

ORPEN, Sir William
British, 1878-1931

A nude girl seated on a bed

Signed and dated l.r.: William Orpen '99
Pen and brown wash, 276 x 214 mm.
Inv. No. 53.3

MM 1986, no. 35.

One of a number of nudes drawn by the
artist in connection with his painting, *The
English nude* (1900, Mildura Art Centre,
Australia). The model is likely to have
been Emily Scobel.

OSTADE, Adriaen van
Dutch, 1610-85

The child and the doll

Signed l.l.: AV:O
Pen and watercolour, 110 x 92 mm.
Inv No. 48.11

B. Schnackenburg, *Adriaen van Ostade,
Isack van Ostade, Zeichnungen und
Aquarelle*, I, 1981, no. 216; MM 1986,
no. 17.

The composition was etched in reverse
by the artist in 1679 [See Prints, p. 135].

Ascribed to
POTTER, Paulus
Dutch, 1625-54

An old horse

Black chalk, 227 x 229 mm.
Inv. No. 48.15

REMBRANDT Harmensz. van Rijn
Dutch, 1606-69

Christ and the Woman of Samaria

Pen and brown ink, 210 x 190 mm.
Inv. No. 40.6

O. Benesch, *The drawings of Rembrandt*,
III, 1955, no. 611; MM 1986, no. 13.

A work of the late 1640s. The subject is
from *John*, iv: 7-26. Rembrandt also
made two etchings of the theme, one
dated 1634, the other 1657 or 1658,
according to state. [See Prints, p. 136].

[REMBRANDT Harmensz. van Rijn]

The Parting of David and Jonathan

Pen and wash, 206 x 268 mm.
Inv. No. 45.13

O. Benesch, *The drawings of Rembrandt*,
I, 1954, no. 74a; W. Sumowski, *Drawings
of the Rembrandt school*, I, 1979, no. 253;
MM 1986, no. 14.

Datable c. 1632/3. The subject, which
was formerly known as *The Reconciliation
of David and Absalom*, is from I *Samuel*,
xx: 41-2. It is treated in other drawings by
the artist, in the Kupferstichkabinett, Berlin,
and the Louvre. The present drawing has
also been attributed to Ferdinand Bol
(1616-80).

[REMBRANDT Harmensz. van Rijn]

A sheet of studies

Pen, brown wash and red chalk,
220 x 233 mm.
Inv. No. 49.10

O. Benesch, *The drawings of Rembrandt*,
II, 1954, no. 340; MM 1986, no. 12; exh.
cat., Berlin, Kupferstichkabinett and
elsewhere, *Rembrandt: the master and
his workshop. Drawings and etchings*,
1991, no. 8; RA 1998, no. 96.

The artist's finest model sheet. Datable
to the mid-1630s. Related etchings (Hind
nos. 145 and 152) are dated 1636 and
1637. Etched with variations by I.J. de
Claussin (1795-1844).

Studio of
REMBRANDT

Study of a nude youth

Inscribed l.l.: Rembrandt
Pen and brown wash, arched top,
274 x 160 mm.
Inv. No. 36.5

O. Benesch, *The drawings of Rembrandt*,
IV, 1955, under no. A55; W. Sumowski,
Drawings of the Rembrandt school, V,
1981, no. 1257 and IX, 1985, under no.
2141; MM 1986, no. 15.

This and a number of other ink and wash
drawings of nude youths once attributed
to Rembrandt can be related to three
etchings by him of c. 1646 (Hind nos.
220-2). The present drawing is very close
in style to five others (Louvre and
Bibliothèque Nationale, Paris; Museum
Boymans-van Beuningen, Rotterdam and
private collections). These may be by
Samuel van Hoogstraten (1627-78).

ROWLANDSON, Thomas
British, 1756-1827

Dressing for a masquerade

Signed and dated l.l.: Rowlandson 1790
Pen and watercolour over pencil,
325 x 438 mm.
Inv. No. 48.9

J. Hayes, *Rowlandson watercolours and drawings*, 1972, no. 72; MM 1986, no. 26.

Another version, with numerous small differences, is illustrated in P. Sabin, *Catalogue of watercolour drawings by Thomas Rowlandson*, London, 1948 (no. 34). A third version, perhaps a copy, was in the exhibition, *English drawings and watercolours*, presented by C. Powney and J. Feilding, London, 1973 (no. 26). Etched by Rowlandson and published by S.W. Fores, 1 April 1790 [See Prints, p. 137].

RUBENS, Peter Paul
Flemish, 1577-1640

Portrait of Helena Fourment (?)

Inscribed l.l.: Rubbens delineavit
Inscribed verso: P.P. Rubens delineavit
Collector's mark: Sir Thomas Lawrence (Lugt 2445).
Black and red chalk heightened with white, 561 x 351 mm.
Inv. No. 36.4

J.S. Held, *Rubens, selected drawings*, I, 1959, under no. 115; J.S. Held, *The oil sketches of Peter Paul Rubens*, I, 1980, under no. 334; MM 1986, no. 9.

Datable c. 1630-5 and closely related to a grisaille sketch of *The Wise Virgins* in a Belgian private collection. The traditional identification of the sitter as the artist's second wife stems from the similarity of her pose and costume to those of Helena Fourment in Rubens' portrait of her with two of her children, now in the Louvre.

SHENG TZU-CHAO
Chinese, active 1310-60

Mountainous landscape

Signed l.l.: Drawn by Sheng Tzu-Chao of
Wu-Tang
Artist's seal l.l.: Sheng Tzu-chao his own
seal
Brush and ink on silk; image size
1468 x 610 mm.
Inv. No. 48.2

STEVENS, Alfred George
British, 1817-75

Study of a nude figure

Red chalk on buff paper, 165 x 164 mm.
Inv. No. 41.5

MM 1986, no. 29

One of numerous preparatory studies for
a decorative frieze at Deysbrook House,
West Derby, Liverpool (now in the
Walker Art Gallery). This was
commissioned in 1847. Other studies
are in the Tate Gallery, the Victoria and
Albert Museum and the Walker Art
Gallery.

Ascribed to
STIMMER, Abel
Swiss, 1542-after 1606

Design for a glass painting

Inscribed on roundel c.l.: T. Stimmer [?];
on shield l.c.: SP [or SB, twice]; and on
verso: Stimmer
Collector's mark: Sir Peter Lely (Lugt 2092).
Pen and grey wash heightened with white
on greenish prepared paper, 334 x 220 mm.
Inv. No. 55.4

Exh. cat., Manchester City Art Gallery,
Between Renaissance and Baroque,
1965, no. 381; MM 1986, no. 8.

Previously ascribed to Tobias Stimmer
(1539-84).

TIEPOLO, Giovanni Battista
Italian, 1696-1770

Zephyrus and Flora

Pen and brown wash over black chalk,
239 x 331 mm.
Inv. No. 36.9

E. Sack, *Giovanni Battista und Domenico
Tiepolo*, 1910, pp. 122, 128, no. 106;
D. von Hadeln, *Handzeichnungen von G.B.
Tiepolo*, I, 1927, p. 13; MM 1986, no. 22.

A study for the ceiling-fresco of the Sala
degli Specchi in the Palazzo Labia,
Venice, completed probably by 1750. A
related oil-sketch was formerly in a
private collection, London. Several other
drawings of the subject by Tiepolo are
recorded.

(recto)   (verso)

TINTORETTO, Jacopo Robusti, called
Italian, 1518-94

Seated man seen from above (recto)

Seated man seen from below (verso)

Inscribed l.r.: G. Tintoretto
Collector's mark: Sir Joshua Reynolds
(Lugt 2364)
Black chalk, 271 x 189 mm.
Inv. No. 36.6

H. Tietze and E. Tietze-Conrat, *The
drawings of the Venetian painters*, 1944,
p. 297, no. 1764 (as workshop); exh. cat.,
Venice, Fondazione Cini, *Disegni veneti
di collezioni inglesi*, 1980, no. 20; MM
1986, no. 7.

TURNER, Joseph Mallord William
British, 1775-1851

Ludlow Castle

Signed l.l.: W. Turner
Watercolour on card, 357 x 572 mm.
Inv. No. 42.8

A. Wilton, *The life and work of J.M.W.
Turner*, 1979, no. 265; MM 1986, no. 27.

Executed in 1800. The view is derived
from a pencil sketch, partly finished in
watercolour, in the Hereford Court
sketchbook of 1798 (British Museum,
T.B. XXXVIII, p. 11a). A larger variant
is in the Huntington Art Gallery, San
Marino.

Ascribed to
VERONESE, Paolo Caliari, called
Italian, 1528-88

Meekness

Pen and brown wash heightened with bodycolour on blue paper, 189 x 310 mm.
Inv. No. 37.2

Related to the ceiling painting of the same subject by Veronese in the Sala del Collegio of the Doge's Palace, Venice. This was executed 1575-7.

WALCOT, William
Anglo-Russian, 1874-1943

The Barber Institute of Fine Arts

Watercolour and bodycolour,
730 x 1355 mm.
Inv. No. 38.15

Exh. cat., London, Dulwich Picture Gallery and elsewhere, *Palaces of Art*, 1991, p. 158, no. F18.

Commissioned by the Trustees of the Barber Institute in September 1938 to mark its completion.

WALKER, Frederick
British, 1840-75

Portrait of the artist

Red chalk heightened with white on buff paper, 496 x 612 mm.
Inv. No. 40.1

On the easel is a study for *The harbour of refuge* (now in the Tate Gallery), exhibited at the Royal Academy in 1872.

SCULPTURE

After
BARYE, Antoine-Louis
French, 1796-1875

Tiger walking

Inscribed on base: BARYE
Bronze, 21.3 x 42.3 cm.
Inv. No. 48.14

S. Pivar, *The Barye bronzes*, 1974, p. 40
(A58); G.F. Benge, *Antoine-Louis Barye:
sculptor of romantic realism*, 1984, p. 85.

Barye's original was made in 1836.

[After
BARYE, Antoine-Louis]

Indian panther

Bronze, 7.3 x 18.5 cm.
Inv. No. 45.9

S. Pivar, *The Barye bronzes*, 1974, p. 41
(A72).

Barye's original was made in 1840.

[After
BARYE, Antoine-Louis]

Theseus and the Centaur

Inscribed on base: BARYE
Bronze, 34.3 x 37.7 cm.
Inv. No. 46.2

S. Pivar, *The Barye bronzes*, 1974, p. 37
(F22); G.F. Benge, *Antoine-Louis Barye:
sculptor of romantic realism*, 1984,
pp. 48-9.

One of a number of casts from Barye's
model for a larger work, commissioned by
the Ministry of the Interior and exhibited in
plaster at the Salon of 1850. A large bronze
version was set up in 1894 as part of the
Barye Memorial, Paris. The subject derives
from Ovid, *Metamorphoses*, xii: 344-9.

After
BOLOGNA, Giovanni
Italian, 1529-1608

Hercules raising his club

Bronze, 41.3 cm. high
Inv. No. 45.4

Exh. cat., London, Arts Council,
Giambologna, sculptor to the Medici,
1978, nos. 84 and 90 (on Louvre and
Bargello versions).

Possibly a late 16th century cast by
Bologna's assistant, Antonio Susini
(active 1580, died 1624). A version in the
Bargello, Florence, may be by Bologna
himself. Other versions show the figure
confronted by Cerberus or a dragon.

[After
BOLOGNA, Giovanni]

A bull

Bronze, 23 x 27.2 cm.
Inv. No. 45.5

Exh. cat., London, Arts Council,
Giambologna, sculptor to the Medici,
1978, nos. 177 and 178 (on Bargello and
Smith College versions).

Perhaps cast in Florence in the late 16th
century. Of the many versions, the only
one accredited to Bologna himself is in
the Bargello, Florence.

[After
BOLOGNA, Giovanni]

Allegorical figure of Astronomy

Bronze, 35 cm. high, including
bronze base
Inv. No. 45.6

Exh. cat., London, Arts Council,
Giambologna, sculptor to the Medici,
1978, no. 12 (on Vienna version);
J. Holderbaum, *The sculptor
Giovanni Bologna*, 1983, pp. 141-3 (on
Vienna version).

A relatively coarse version, perhaps
German or Flemish, of the late 16th
century. Bologna's slightly larger gilt
bronze, probably made in the mid-1570s, is
in the Kunsthistorisches Museum, Vienna.

After
BOLTEN, Arent van
Dutch, c. 1573–after 1633?

Lamp in the form of a grotesque bird

Bronze, 17 cm. high
Inv. No. 43.7

Exh. cat., Manchester City Art Gallery,
Between Renaissance and Baroque, 1965,
no. 442; J. Leeuwenberg, *Apollo*, LXXXIII,
1966, p. 273.

Probably made in the 17th century. There
are versions in the Victoria and Albert
Museum, the Rijksmuseum, Amsterdam,
the Bayerisches Nationalmuseum, Munich,
and elsewhere.

CHINARD, Joseph
French, 1756-1813

Bust of Madame Récamier

Marble, 67.3 cm. high, including socle
Inv. No. 50.15

Exh. cat., London, Arts Council, *The age
of Neo-classicism*, 1972, no. 346 (on
Rhode Island version).

Datable c. 1802. Juliette Récamier
(1777-1849) was the wife of a wealthy
banker and a prominent figure in Parisian
political and literary circles. There are a
number of other versions. The principal
examples in marble are in the Musée des
Beaux-Arts, Lyon, and the Museum of
Art, Rhode Island School of Design,
Providence, RI.

CHINESE

c. 10th/11th century

Head of a Boddhisattva

Limestone, with traces of paint
58.4 cm. high
Inv. No. 43.3

Probably a fragment from a whole figure. A Boddhisattva is one who has reached the transcendent wisdom of the Buddha, but remains in the world and does not enter nirvana from compassion for earthly creatures, and as a means of salvation.

After
DALOU, Jules
French, 1838-1902

Meleager

Inscribed l.r.: DALOU
Foundry mark l.r.: CIRE/PERDUE/
A A HEBRARD
Bronze, 63.9 cm. high
Inv. No. 64.3

Exh. cat., London, Mallett at Bourdon House, *Sculptures by Jules Dalou*, 1964, no. 78; J.M. Hunisak, *The sculptor Jules Dalou*, 1977, p. 120.

Cast no. 6, out of a probable ten, taken posthumously from a plaster model (now in the Petit Palais, Paris) for an unfulfilled commission of 1898 from the duc de Gramont.

After
DEGAS, Hilaire-Germain-Edgar
French, 1834-1917

Horse trotting

Inscribed on base: degas
Foundry mark on base: CIRE/PERDUE/
A A HEBRARD
Bronze, 22.5 x 22.2 cm., including base
Inv. No. 50.3

J. Rewald, *Degas, works in sculpture*, 1956, no. IV.

Cast no. 11/T out of 22 taken posthumously between 1919 and 1921 from the original wax model by Degas, now in a private collection. Often entitled *Horse walking*, but the action is of a formal trot.

[After
DEGAS, Hilaire-Germain-Edgar]

Grande arabesque, third time

Inscribed on base: degas
Foundry mark on base: CIRE/PERDUE/
A A HEBRARD
Bronze, 44.5 x 55.3 cm., including base
Inv. No. 42.1

J. Rewald, *Degas, works in sculpture*,
1956, no. XXXIX; BMAG 1991, pp. 28-9.

Cast no. 60/F out of 22 taken posthumously
between 1919 and 1921 from the original
wax model by Degas, now in the Louvre.

[After
DEGAS, Hilaire-Germain-Edgar]

*Dancer ready to dance, the right foot
forward*

Inscribed on base: degas
Foundry mark on base: CIRE/PERDUE/
A A HEBRARD
Bronze, 56.5 cm. high, including base
Inv. No. 48.17

J. Rewald, *Degas, works in sculpture*,
1956, no. XLVI.

Cast no. 57/J out of 22 taken posthumously
between 1919 and 1921 from the original
wax model by Degas, now in a private
collection.

After
DONATELLO
Italian, c. 1386-1466

An angel playing an aulos

Bronze relief, 58 x 21.9 cm.
Inv. No. 50.10

H.W. Janson, *The sculpture of Donatello*,
II, 1957, pp. 162-87 (on the high altar of
San Antonio).

Based on one of the twelve bronze reliefs
of music-making angels that make up the
predella of the high altar of San Antonio
at Padua in its modern form. They were
largely made in 1447 by Donatello's
assistants. A number of simplified copies
such as this one are known, some datable
to the 16th century, but none before.

EGYPTIAN

15th/14th century BC

Head of Amenhotep III

Gabbro, 60 x 46.5 cm.
Inv. No. 44.1

B.V. Bothmer in *Papers presented at the international symposium held at the Cleveland Museum of Art, 20-21 November 1987*, p. 87.

From a lost colossal statue of the pharaoh. There are traces of colouring in the eyes, lips and crown.

ENGLISH

14th/15th century

The Coronation of the Virgin

Alabaster relief, with polychrome and gilt 103 x 58.5 cm.
Inv. No. 39.25

F. Cheetham, *English medieval alabasters*, 1984, under no.135.

Made in Nottingham and originally painted, this relief is unusual for its large size. A comparable smaller alabaster is in the Victoria and Albert Museum.

FLEMISH

16th century

The Meeting of Joachim and Anna

Wood, 55.9 x 40.3 cm.
Inv. No. 40.10

The subject comes from *The Golden Legend*, cxxix.

FRENCH(?)
15th century
A woman mourning
Marble, 14.8 cm. high.
Inv. No. 58.3

After
**GÉRICAULT, Jean-Louis-André-
Théodore**
French, 1791-1824
Anatomical model of a horse
Foundry mark on base: CIRE/
C. VALSUANI/PERDUE
Bronze, 22.8 x 21.7 cm., including base
Inv. No. 60.6

Exh. cat., Paris, Grand Palais, *Géricault*,
1991, under no. 25.

The third of 15 casts (plus five 'hors
commerce') taken in 1959 from the
wax model by Géricault (c. 1817-23,
private collection). A plaster is in the
Louvre and a related drawing in the
Musée Bonnat, Bayonne.

GERMAN
16th century
St Catherine (?)
Wood, painted and gilt, 71.1 cm. high
Inv. No. 44.5

Exh. cat., Manchester City Art Gallery,
German art 1400-1800, 1961, no. 48.

Probably made in Swabia c. 1520. The
left hand is restored.

GERMAN (?)
18th century

A rhinoceros

Bronze, 24.5 x 46.7 cm.
Inv. No. 42.9

T.H. Clarke, *The rhinoceros from Dürer to Stubbs, 1515-1799*, 1986, pp. 115-6.

Probably made c. 1750. A French origin is as likely. There are bronze replicas in the Victoria and Albert Museum and the Louvre. Marble and ceramic versions also exist.

GRECO-ROMAN
1st century BC/AD

Torso of Aphrodite

Marble, 58.1 cm. high
Inv. No. 40.9

A comparable figure, from Ostia, is in the British Museum

GREEK
5th century BC

Head of a woman

Marble, 21.1 cm. high
Inv. No. 61.6

Exh. cat., London, Royal Academy, *Greek art*, 1946, no. 157.

Perhaps carved c. 445 BC, and detached from a relief.

GREEK
4th century BC
Head of Aphrodite
Marble, 19 cm. high
Inv. No. 45.10

INDIAN
15th/16th century
Siva as Lord of Dance
Bronze, 78 x 69.2 cm.
Inv. No. 46.3
From south India. The Hindu deity performs the mystic Dance of Creation.

ITALIAN
13th century
Lion mask
Marble, 33.4 x 31.5 cm.
Inv. No. 68.5
A fountain head, perhaps Tuscan.

ITALIAN
15th century

Prudence

Marble, 26.3 cm. high
Inv. No. 64.1

Probably a fragment from a tomb of the
early 15th century, perhaps from the
church of S. Francesco, Gaeta.

ITALIAN
15th century (?)

A female saint

Marble, 50.3 cm. high
Inv. No. 48.8

Perhaps Sienese. At her right shoulder is
part of a martyr's palm.

ITALIAN
15th/16th century (?)

Bust of a youth

Polychromed terracotta, 43.1 x 46.4 cm.
Inv. No. 50.11

Related to a bust of St Ansanus in a
terracotta roundel by Andrea della
Robbia (1435-1525) in the Museo
Bandini, Fiesole, but much restored.

ITALIAN
16th century

A soldier on horseback

Bronze, 15.3 x 15.5 cm., excluding
marble base
Inv. No. 45.11

A.C. Sewter, *The Connoisseur*, CXXIV,
1949, p. 28.

The figure was probably intended as
St George, the right hand holding a spear
which was thrust into a crouching dragon.

[ITALIAN
16th century]

A Roman soldier on horseback

Bronze, 26.4 x 25.6 cm., excluding
wooden pedestal
Inv. No. 45.12

A.C. Sewter, *The Connoisseur*, CXXIV,
1949, p. 27.

The rider is cast separately. There are a
number of examples of the horse alone,
including two finer versions in the Wallace
Collection and the Museo Estense,
Modena.

[ITALIAN
16th century]

A boy with a dolphin

Bronze, 51.5 cm. high, including pedestal
Inv. No. 45.7

A.C. Sewter, *The Connoisseur*, CXXIV,
1949, p. 28.

A fountain head, of late 16th century
origin and formerly ascribed to Jacopo
Sansovino (1486-1570).

ITALIAN
16th century (?)

Hercules and a dragon (?)

Wax and cartapesta, 28.4 cm. high
Inv. No. 50.8

W. Bode, *The Italian bronze statuettes of the Renaissance*, I, 1907, p. 44.

An attribution to the Florentine sculptor, Giovanni Francesco Rustici (1475-1554), has been proposed.

ITALIAN
17th century

The drunken Silenus

Bronze, 24.7 x 22.6 cm.
Inv. No. 48.4

A.C. Sewter, *The Connoisseur*, CXXIV, 1949, p. 24.

Probably Venetian, of the early 17th century. An inferior variant is recorded in W. Bode, *The Italian bronze statuettes of the Renaissance*, III, 1912, p. 15.

ITALIAN
17th/18th century

The Punishment of Dirce

Bronze, 42.9 cm. high
Inv. No. 48.3

A.C. Sewter, *The Connoisseur*, CXXIV, 1949, pp. 25-6 (as by Francesco Susini).

One of many small reproductions and variations in bronze of the celebrated antique marble known as *The Farnese Bull* (Museo Nazionale, Naples). The subject was known in antiquity chiefly through a lost tragedy of Euripides. Dirce was tied to a wild bull by the two sons of Antiope for her cruelty to their mother.

After
MADERNO, Stefano
Italian, c. 1576-1636

Hercules and the Nemean Lion

Wood, 33.8 x 30.3 cm., including base
Inv. No. 50.9

I. Robertson, *Burl. Mag.*, LXIX, 1936,
pp. 176-7 (then in the H. Harris
collection).

Possibly of German origin. Maderno's
original, a larger terracotta, dated 1621
is in the Cà d'Oro, Venice. A number of
bronze versions are known. The subject
was the first of the Labours of Hercules.

Ascribed to
MAUCH, Daniel
German, 1477-1540

St Dorothy

Wood, painted and gilt, 56 cm. high
Inv. No. 43.8

Exh. cat., Manchester City Art Gallery,
German art 1400-1800, 1961, no. 72.

Made at Ulm c. 1510. St Dorothy of
Caesarea was martyred in 304.

Workshop of
NOST, John the elder
Anglo-Flemish, active 1686-d. 1710

King George I on horseback

Bronze, 290 x 278.5 cm.
Inv. No. 37.14

M.D. Whinney, *Sculpture in Britain 1530 to 1830*, 1988, p. 134; S. O'Connell, *Burl. Mag.*, CXXIX, 1987, pp. 803-4; P. Spencer-Longhurst and A. Naylor, *The Sculpture Journal*, II, 1998, pp. 31-40.

Commissioned in 1717, when Nost himself was dead. The execution was probably by Andrew Carpenter (c.1677-1737) and C. Burchard (active 1716). Erected in Dublin on Essex Bridge in 1722. A lead version is at Stowe School, Buckinghamshire. Another version, also in lead, showing the king in Roman armour, is at Hackwood Park, Hampshire.

PERSIAN
5th century BC

Head of a spearman

Limestone relief, 26.1 x 24.1 cm.
Inv. No. 47.7

A fragment from a frieze depicting palace guards, probably from the palace of Persepolis.

Ascribed to
RICCIO, Andrea
Italian, 1470-1532

A negro riding a goat

Bronze, 21.7 x 22.1 cm., excluding base
Inv. No. 43.2

J. Fletcher, *Journal of the Warburg and Courtauld Institutes*, XXXVI, 1973, p. 383, n. 19; exh. cat., Frankfurt, Liebighaus Museum alter Plastiker, *Natur und Antike in der Renaissance*, 1985, no. 182.

Apparently a unique piece. It has also been ascribed to Severo da Ravenna (active at Padua c. 1500). The base is French 18th century.

Ascribed to
ROBBIA, Giovanni della
Italian, 1469-1529/30

Madonna and Child

Polychromed and glazed terracotta, 137 x 95 cm., including terracotta frame
Inv. No. 42.2

A. Marquand, *Giovanni della Robbia*, 1920, no. 128.

Said to have come from the Carmelite church at Castellina, near Florence, which was built by 1506.

After
RODIN, Auguste
French, 1840-1917

The Age of Bronze

Inscribed on base: Rodin
Foundry mark on base: Alexis.
RUDIER./Fondeur.PARIS
Bronze, 180.5 cm. high, including
bronze base
Inv. No. 42.2

A. Elsen, *Rodin*, 1963, pp. 20-6; J.L.
Tancock, *The sculpture of Auguste Rodin*,
1976, pp. 342-56.

Begun in 1875. The plaster was exhibited
in Brussels in 1877, as *Le Vaincu*; then
under its present title at the Paris Salon
(no. 4107). It is now in the Musée Rodin,
Paris. A bronze cast was shown at the
Salon of 1880 (no. 6640). There are
numerous other bronze casts of various
sizes and periods but the present one is
likely to have been made before Rodin's
death. An autograph drawing of the
composition, of c. 1880, is in the Louvre.

[After (?)
RODIN, Auguste]

Bust of Henri Rochefort

Marble, 81.3 cm. high
Inv. No. 38.3

F. Lawton, *The life and work of Auguste
Rodin*, 1906, pp. 90-1; F. Grunfeld,
Rodin: a biography, 1988, pp. 161-3;
J. Newton, *Laurels*, vol. 58, no. 3, 1987-8,
pp. 181, 184, n. 2.

A plaster version exhibited in 1886 was
presumably that now in the Musée
Rodin, Paris, from which bronze casts
have been made. The present version was
probably executed by Rodin's marble-
cutter, Henri Lebossé, in 1898. Victor
Henri, marquis de Rochefort-Luçay
(1830-1913) was a radical journalist, art
collector and patron.

ROMAN
1st century AD

Head of a man

Marble, 34.1 cm. high
Inv. No. 62.8

ROMAN
2nd century AD

Head of a bearded man

Marble, 40.2 cm. high
Inv. No. 62.9

ROUBILIAC, Louis-François
Anglo-French 1702/5-62

Bust of Alexander Pope

Terracotta, 62.1 cm. high, including socle
Inv. No. 70.6

W. Wimsatt, *The portraits of Alexander Pope*, 1965, no. 57.1 (then in the Copner collection); exh. cat., London, Victoria and Albert Museum, *Rococo. Art and design in Hogarth's England*, 1984, no. S4.

Alexander Pope, poet and critic, lived from 1688 to 1744. This is almost certainly the original life-model for the four signed marble versions. The first of these is dated 1738 (Temple Newsam, Leeds). An early plaster cast of the terracotta is in the British Museum, and there are other derivatives.

SCANDINAVIAN (?)
16th century

*Christ with Saints John the Baptist,
Peter, Catherine, Barbara, James the
Great and James the Less*

Wood relief, 53.4 x 161.5 cm., excluding
modern border
Inv. No. 50.18

Perhaps taken from the front of a chest.

Ascribed to
TACCA, Pietro
Italian, 1580-1650

A pacing horse

Bronze, 30.7 x 33.5 cm.
Inv. No. 48.13

A.C. Sewter, *The Connoisseur*, CXXIV,
1949, p. 26

A Florentine type of the early 17th
century, and very close to the horse in the
small equestrian bronze of *Philip IV of
Spain*, ascribed to Tacca, in the Detroit
Institute of Arts. A repetition, with a
bronze base, is in a private collection.

After
TARGONE, Cesare
Italian, active 1573(?)-85

*The Madonna mourning the dead
Christ*

Bronze relief, 28.3 x 26.1 cm.
Inv. No. 50.4

Closely based on a repoussé gold relief,
recorded in the London art market in
1983, the only signed and certain work
by Targone. The composition recurs in a
relief on the base of *The Assumption*
(c. 1586-7), by Annibale Fontana, in the
church of S. Maria presso S. Celso,
Milan.

THAI

15th century

Head of a Buddha

Bronze, with traces of gilt, 20.6 cm. high
Inv. No. 42.3

R. Le May, *A concise history of Buddhist art in Siam*, 1938, p. 141.

Probably from a complete figure, executed in the south-central region of the country.

THAI

16th century

Head of Buddha

Bronze, 33.5 cm. high
Inv. No. 42.7

R. Le May, *A concise history of Buddhist art in Siam*, 1938, p. 148.

In a style associated with the capital city of Ayutthaya. Probably taken from a complete figure.

After
WARIN, Jean
French, 1607-72

Bust of Cardinal Richelieu

Bronze, 69.8 cm. high
Inv. No. 67.1

F. Mazerolle, *Jean Varin*, I 1932, no. 213
(on the commission and other versions);
F. Pény, *Jean Varin de Liège 1607-72*,
1947, pp. 33-5.

Possibly one of the four casts after
Warin's plaster model (1641, now lost) for
which Hubert Le Sueur was paid in 1643,
or one of the two further bronzes made
the same year by Henri Perlan. Other
casts are in the Bibliothèque Mazarine
and the Musée Jacquemart-André, Paris;
the Albertinum, Dresden; and Windsor
Castle. Armand Jean du Plessis, Cardinal
Richelieu (1585-1642) was First Minister
of France under Louis XIII.

WEST AFRICAN
18th/19th century

An altarpiece

Brass, 21.3 cm. high, 26.7 cm. diameter
at base
Inv. No. 48.1

Made at Benin, Nigeria, for the altar of a
queen mother.

ART OBJECTS
FURNITURE
&
DECORATIVE ART

BYZANTINE
11th century

St Theodore

Inscribed u.l.: A [within a circle];
r.: ΘΕΟΔWPOC [vertically]
Steatite relief, 6 x 3.2 cm., including
silver frame
Inv. No. 70.2

H. Longuet, *Introduction à la numismatique byzantine*, 1961, pl. XXIV.

St Theodore, a Roman soldier of unknown date, set fire to the Temple of Cybele, and was then martyred.

CHINESE
c. 11th/12th century BC

Wine beaker (ku)

Bronze, 28.6 cm. high
Inv. No. 41.4

CHINESE
c. 10th/11th century BC

Wine beaker (ku)

Bronze, 26 cm. high
Inv. No. 41.3

Exh. cat., London, Royal Academy,
Chinese art, 1935-6, no. 184.

CHINESE
16th century

Box of double-lozenge shape

Inscribed beneath with the mark of
Lung Ch'ing
Lacquer on wood, 12.5 cm. high,
25.4 cm. long, 16.4 cm. wide
Inv. No. 41.6

F. Low-Beer, *Bulletin of the Museum
of Far Eastern Antiquities, Stockholm,*
XXIV, 1952, p. 33.

Apparently the only lacquer with a mark
attaching it to the workshop of the
Emperor Lung Ch'ing (reigned 1567-72).

CHINESE
17th/18th century

*Flask, the cover modelled on the head
of a goose*

Cloisonné enamel on metal, 30.1 cm. high
Inv. No. 46.12

CHINESE
18th century

Vase

White jade, 10.4 cm. high, 12.1 cm. square at the top
Inv. No. 40.7

W.Watson, *Apollo*, LIII, 1951, p. 104.

[CHINESE
18th century]

Bowl

Incised inscription inside (see below)
Grey-green jade, oval, 10.5 cm. high, 25.7 cm. long, 21 cm. wide
Inv. No. 45.1

The inscription may in part be translated: 'The large piece of jade was a tribute sent from Khotan [...] The design resembles the superb paintings of Seng-yu [...] Written by the Emperor Ch'ien Lung in the cyclical year Chia-wa [AD 1774].'

ENGLISH
17th century

The Butleigh Salt

Maker's mark: M H [in monogram]
London 1606/7
Silver gilt, 31.1 cm. high, base 15.5 cm. square
Inv. No. 49.3

P. Glanville, *Silver in Tudor and early Stuart England*, 1990, p. 288; exh. cat., Antwerp, Provinciaal Museum Sterckshof-Zilvercentrum *Zilver voor Sir Anthony*, 1999, no. 11.

An elaborate salt-cellar, so called from its long association with Butleigh Court near Glastonbury.

[ENGLISH
17th century]

Trestle table

Oak, 85 cm. high, 795 cm. long,
111.5 cm. wide
Inv. No. 47.8

R.W. Symonds, *The Antique Collector*,
VIII, 1937, p. 274.

Early 17th century, from Highclere
Castle, Berkshire.

[ENGLISH
17th century]

Cabinet on stand

Walnut with seaweed marquetry,
167 cm. high, 113.7 cm. wide,
54 cm. deep
Inv. No. 42.6

Made at the end of the century.

ENGLISH
18th century

Tea pot and stand

Hall mark: London 1785
Maker's mark: $\frac{DS}{RS}$
Gold with wood handle and bone knob,
pot 12.6 cm. high, 24.5 cm. long (oval);
stand 1.7 cm. high, 15.9 cm. long (oval)
Inv. No. 48.18

A. Grimwade, *The Connoisseur*,
CXXVIII, 1951, pp. 86-7; M. Snodin
and M. Baker, *Burl. Mag.*, CXXII, 1980,
p. 835 (A17).

Engraved with the arms of the writer and
wealthy eccentric, William Beckford
(1759-1844) and his wife, Lady Margaret
Gordon. The makers were Robert Sharp
and Daniel Smith.

[ENGLISH
18th century]

Cabinet

Mahogany and parcel gilt, 94.2 cm. high,
133.4 cm. long, 60.6 cm. deep, including
marble top
Inv. No. 53.4

Mid-century, in the style of William Kent
(1684-1756).

[ENGLISH
18th century]

Settee with tapestry covering

Walnut, 93.7 cm. high, 162.5 cm. wide,
81.5 cm. deep
Inv. No. 42.5

The tapestry is possibly by William
Bradshaw (active 1728-75), of the Soho
workshop, to a design by Tobias
Stranover (1684-1756).

[ENGLISH
18th century]

Dining chair

Walnut, 103.7 cm. high, 52.2 cm. wide,
42 cm. deep
Inv. No. 38.2

Datable c. 1720. The inlaid monogram
on the splat is composed of the initials
PD, and the same reversed.

ENGLISH
19th century

Bloodstone bowl and setting

Hall mark: London 1824
Maker's mark: PS
Silver gilt and bloodstone, 22.7 cm. high,
19.8 cm. long, 12.8 cm. wide, including
bowl
Inv. No. 54.5

M. Snodin and M. Baker, *Burl. Mag.*,
CXXII, 1980, pp. 820, 835 (A101).
C. Wainwright, *The Romantic interior*,
1989, pp. 144, 146.

The setting is by Paul Storr (1771-1844),
a celebrated London goldsmith, but the
bowl may be some 200 years older.
Included in a painting of *Objects of Vertu*
by Willes Maddox (1844, Beckford
Tower Trust), together with other objects
from the collection of William Beckford.

Imitation of
ETRUSCAN

Helmet

Bronze, 20.1 cm. high, 27 cm. long
25 cm. wide
Inv. No. 53.2

FRENCH
12th century

*Christ in Majesty with symbols of the
Four Evangelists*

Champlevé enamel on metal,
23.3 x 10.4 cm.
Inv. No. 49.6

Made in Limoges at the end of the
century as the back central plaque of
a book binding. Of the numerous
comparable examples the closest is
in the British Museum.

FRENCH
13th century

Crozier head in the form of a serpent

Metal with cloisonné enamel, 14.6 cm.
high, excluding modern mount
Inv. No. 50.16

Made at Limoges c. 1205-15. A number
of comparable examples are known.

[FRENCH
13th century]

Pyx

Metal with champlevé enamel,
10.6 cm. high, 6.6 cm. diameter
Inv. No. 45.8

Perhaps made c. 1240-60. The cross was
probably added in the following century.
A container for carrying the eucharistic
wafer to the sick.

FRENCH
14th century

Wing of a diptych with St John the Baptist and other figures

Ivory relief with traces of gilding and colour, 7.8 x 5.4 cm.
Inv. No. 48.5

The left wing is missing. The other figures have not been identified.

[FRENCH
14th century]

Casket with scenes of chivalry and love

Ivory, 9.5 cm. high, 23.2 cm. long, 13.6 cm. wide, excluding metal fittings
Inv. No. 39.26

A. McL. Young, *The Connoisseur*, CXX, 1947, pp. 16-21.

One of eight such caskets known to have survived complete. The lid shows a tournament; the front, Aristotle and Phyllis, and Pyramus and Thisbe (twice); the left side, Tristan and Iseult, and the capture of the Unicorn; the right side, the knight, Enyas, delivering a maiden from a wild man of the woods; the back, four episodes from the adventures of Gawain and Lancelot.

Imitation of
FRENCH
14th century

Mirror back carved with a tournament scene

Ivory relief, circular, 8.4 cm. diameter, excluding four pierced lions on the rim.
Inv. No. 50.14

FRENCH
16th century

A pair of candlesticks

One signed: .P.R [Pierre Reymond]
Painted enamel on metal, each 35.9 cm.
high
Inv. Nos. 46.7 a & b

From the workshop of Pierre Reymond
(1513-84?) at Limoges. The scenes on the
bases principally depict the Golden Calf
(*Exodus*, xxxii) and the Brazen Serpent
(*Numbers*, xxi: 4-9).

FRENCH
18th century

Commode

Stamped: [twice] LARDIN, M.E. [and
ten times] C. CHEVALLIER
Marquetry on tulip wood with ormulu,
86.7 cm. high, 146.3 cm. long, 66.3 cm.
deep, including grey marble top
Inv. No. 38.13

Datable between 1750, when André
Antoine Lardon became a member of the
guild of furniture-makers (*menuisiers-
ébénistes*) in Paris, and 1771, when his
collaborator, Charles Chevallier the
younger, died.

[FRENCH
18th century]

Commode

Stamped twice: M.CARLIN
Parquetry on harewood ground, with
ormulu, 88 cm. high, 114 cm. long,
58.8 cm. deep
Inv. No. 38.14

Martin Carlin became a member of the
guild of furniture-makers (*menuisiers-
ébénistes*) in Paris in 1766 and died in
1785.

GERMAN

13th century

Aquamanile in the form of a knight on horseback

Bronze, 31.7 cm. high, 29 cm. long
Inv. No. 49.7

O. von Falke and E. Meyer, *Romanische Leuchter [...] Bronzegeräte des Mittelalters*, I, 1935, p. 46, no. 296.

Probably from Hildesheim. Used in the rinsing of hands at table.

[GERMAN

13th century]

Arm reliquary

Wood overlaid with silver, decorated with gilt copper filigree and semi-precious stones, 49.8 cm. high
Inv. No. 61.9

Made in the Rhineland, c.1200-25. There are early repairs, and the ring, which bears a worn and unintelligible inscription, is probably 15th century.

GERMAN

16th century

A rearing unicorn

Maker's mark: HE [joined]; also the mark of the city of Constance and an unidentified mark
Silver gilt, 35.8 cm. high
Inv. No. 37.5

Made at Constance c. 1575-1600 by Heinrich Eglof. A drinking vessel – the head and upper neck are detachable.

GERMAN
16th/17th century

Combed morion

Armourer's marks, unidentified
Steel, etched and gilded, 29.1 cm. high,
33.9 cm. long, 23.8 cm. wide, excluding
chin-straps
Inv. No. 51.6

A helmet of the guard of the Elector
Christian II of Saxony (1591-1611). On
the comb are the arms of Saxony and the
insignia of the arch-marshalcy of the
Holy Roman Empire; below are figures
of Marcus Curtius and Mucius Scaevola.

GERMAN
17th century

A lion rampant

Maker's mark on base: PS
City mark on base: N
Silver gilt, 32 cm. high
Inv. No. 37.6

Made at Nuremberg c. 1650. A drinking
vessel - the upper part of the head is
detachable.

GREEK
7th/6th century BC

Helmet

Bronze, 23.3 cm. high, 27.1 cm. long,
19.6 cm. wide
Inscribed on left cheekpiece: ζενὸς
'Ολυνπίου [in archaic script]
Inv. No. 49.11

J. Stuart and N. Revett, *Antiquities of
Athens*, IV, 1830, p. 30; E. Kukahn,
Der Griechische Helm, 1936, no. 53;
E. Kunze, *VII Bericht über die
Ausgrabungen in Olympia*, 1961, no. 23.

Corinthian, said to have been found at
Olympia. The inscription means 'Sacred
to Olympian Zeus'.

IRISH
11th/6th century BC

Torc

Gold, 16.6 cm. diameter
Inv. No. 43.4

J.J. Taylor, *Bronze age goldwork*, 1980, p. 104 (CoDn 38)

A neck ornament, reputedly found in Carrowdore Bog, Co. Down.

ITALIAN
12th century

Crucifix

Bronze, 32.7 cm. high, 22.1 cm. wide
Inv. No. 49.5

Perhaps made in Tuscany c. 1125-50. Incised with the Madonna, St John and an angel on the recto, and symbols of the Four Evangelists and the Lamb of God on the verso.

ITALIAN
16th century

The Man of Sorrows

Inscribed in the lunette: QUI.TOLIT. PECCATA.MONDI
Bronze, arched top, 16.6 x 10.7 cm.
Inv. No. 50.4

A pax, or tablet used to convey the kiss of peace at Mass.

ROMAN
1st century BC/AD

Head of a dog

Bronze, 10.7 cm. high, 14.5 cm. long
Inv. No. 51.3

An ornament from the head-rest or
foot-board of a couch.

SPANISH
16th century

Close helmet

Steel, 37.5 cm. high, 36.3 cm. long,
26.7 cm. wide
Inv. No. 51.6

Made in the later part of the century.

SPANISH
17th century

Christ at the Column

Ivory, 22.8 cm. high
Inv. No. 50.12

PORTRAIT
MINIATURES

HILLIARD, Nicholas
British, 1547-1619

Portrait of a man

Watercolour on vellum, oval,
61 x 51 mm., including frame
Inv. No. 55.26

E. Auerbach, *Nicholas Hilliard*, 1961,
no. 170; exh. cat., Edinburgh, Scottish
Arts Council, *A kind of gentle painting*,
1975, no. 36.

Datable c. 1610-15, the frame c. 1700.

INDIAN, Deccani School
17th century

Portrait of Sultan Ali Adil Shah II

Inscribed in Persian u.c.: Ibrahim Adil
Shah of Bijapur
Miniature, 389 x 237 mm., including
border
Inv. No. 47.4

M. Zebrowski, *Deccani Paintings*, 1983,
p. 140

Bijapur, datable c. 1660. *Pace* the
inscription the sitter is Ali Adil Shah II,
who reigned 1656-72. On the verso, in
Arabic calligraphy decorated with
flowers, is the last verse of the Koran,
signed, Sultan Muhammad Nowzar.

INDIAN, Moghul School
18th century

Portrait of the Emperor Ahmad Shah

Miniature 437 x 296 mm., including
border
Inv. No. 47.5

The Moghul Emperor Ahmad Shah
reigned 1748-54. On the verso, in
illuminated Persian calligraphy, is a verse
roughly translated as: 'Always with good
auspices occupy the throne of Alexander
the Great, like Khizr live long, and have
wine always in your glass.' [Signed]
Muhammad Shafi' Ghaffrolla Dombeh.

INDIAN, Moghul School
18th century

Portrait of a lady

Miniature 216 x 138 mm., including
border
Inv. No. 47.6

The subject may be a Ragini, or musical
mode.

OLIVER, Isaac
British, c. 1565-1617

Portrait of Henry, Prince of Wales

Signed c.l.: IO [in monogram]
Watercolour on vellum, oval,
55 x 46 mm., including frame
Inv. No. 49.4

R. Strong, *National Portrait Gallery
catalogues. Tudor and Jacobean
portraits*, I, 1969, p. 164

Painted c. 1610 and originally in the
Royal Collection. Prince Henry (1594-
1612) wears the ribbon of the Garter.
Several related miniatures are known,
including one in the Royal Collection.

RIZĀ-I-'ABBĀSĪ
Persian, active 1618-34

A seated dervish

Signed u.l.: The work of the humble
Riẕa 'Abbasī
Black ink on buff paper, sheet size
220 x 195 mm.
Inv. No. 49.2

On the verso is a poem in Persian
calligraphy, translatable as: 'Do not be
a companion with one lower than thyself,
because a wise person converses with
those better than himself. Do not be
pressing with a person greater than
thyself, for he too does not wish to be
in company lesser than himself.'

MANUSCRIPTS

(fol. 15 recto)

FRENCH
14th century

Book of Hours

152 vellum leaves including 36 miniatures in a richly tooled binding perhaps of c. 1600
Leaf size, 128 x 92 mm.
Inv. No. 59.11

N. R. Ker, *Medieval manuscripts in British libraries*, II, 1977, p. 78.

Contains the Hours of the Virgin, according to the use of Metz, with a calendar.

(fol. 16 recto)

ITALIAN
c. 1480

Book of Hours

227 vellum leaves including 32 miniatures in a 19th century binding.
Leaf size, 140 x 86 mm.
Inv. No. 69.7

N. R. Ker, *Medieval manuscripts in British libraries*, II, 1977, pp. 78-9.

Once the property of Cardinal Domenico della Rovere (1442-1501), Bishop of Turin, who was probably the original owner.

LIBERALE da Verona
Italian, c. 1445-c. 1526

Christ in Glory

Miniature on vellum, sheet size
274 x 215 mm.
Inv. No. 60.2

H. Brigstocke, *The Connoisseur*,
CLXXXIV, 1973, pp. 242, 244; H. J.
Eberhardt, *Sull' attività senese di
Liberale da Verona . . .* , in *La miniatura
italiana tra Gotico e Rinascimento*, Atti
del II congresso di storia della miniatura
italiana, Cortona, 1982, pp. 420-2; exh.
cat., London, Royal Academy, *The
painted page*, 1994, no. 122.

The trial miniature executed by the artist
prior to his work on the Siena Cathedral
choir books in 1467. On the verso are
fragments of plainchant notation and
text.

Studio of the
MASTER OF THE BOUCICAUT
HOURS
French, active c. 1405-15

The Flight into Egypt

Illuminated manuscript on vellum, sheet
size 178 x 132 mm.
Inv. No. 69.6

M. Meiss, *French painting in the time of
Jean de Berry: the Limbourgs*, I, 1974,
p. 458, n. 322; MM 1986, no. 1.

A leaf from a dismembered book of
hours executed in Paris in 1408, of which
it was fol. 52 verso. The text, which
continues from the recto, forms part of
the Vespers of the Virgin. There is a full-
page version of the image in the autograph
Boucicaut Hours in the Musée
Jacquemart-André, Paris. A number of
other versions in the Master's style are
known.

BELLICARD, Jérôme and
COCHIN, Charles
French 1726-86 and 1715-90

*Architectonographie ou cours
universal d'architecture civile
hydraulique et militaire par ordre
alphabétique.*

Manuscript title-page and text of 132
leaves, frontispiece and 219 drawings in
watercolour, pen, red chalk, pencil and
wash in an 18th century binding.
Quarto, leaf size 205 x 153 mm.
Inv. No. 50.17

Dated 1762. Apparently a project for an
unpublished dictionary of architecture.
Five official papers relating to the
Bellicard family accompany the book.

PRINTS

ABBREVIATIONS

Abbreviations of the standard reference-works which have been used are as follows:

Bartsch   A. Bartsch, *Le peintre-graveur*, 1803-21.
Delteil   L. Delteil, *Le peintre-graveur illustré*, 1906-26.
Hollstein   F. Hollstein, *Dutch and Flemish etchings, engravings and woodcuts*, 1949-
Le Blanc   C. Le Blanc, *Manuel de l'amateur d'estampes*, 1854-89.
Robert-Dumesnil A. Robert-Dumesnil, *Le peintre-graveur*, 1835-71.

ANONYMOUS

A new edition, considerably enlarged,
of Attitudes faithfully copied from Nature...

12 engravings bound with title page and
preface, 1807. Caricatures of T. Piroli's
Drawings faithfully copied from Nature at
Naples
Inv. No. 64.6b
[See also Piroli, p. 136]

ANDREANI, Andrea
Italian, c. 1560-1623

The Madonna and Child with putti,
St Sebastian and another saint

Chiaroscuro woodcut after F. Barocci, 1605
Bartsch XII, p. 66, no. 26
Inv. No. 39.2

[ANDREANI, Andrea]

Hercules and the Nemean Lion

Chiaroscuro woodcut after Raphael
Bartsch XII, p. 119, no. 17
Inv. No. 55.20

ANTONIO da Trento
Italian, c. 1508-after 1550

The Tiburtine Sibyl and Augustus

Chiaroscuro woodcut after Parmigianino
Bartsch XII, p. 90, no. 7
Inv. No. 58.2

BAZICALUVA, Ercole
Italian, c. 1600-after 1641

Triumphal carriages in the Piazza dei Cavalieri, Pisa

Etching
Bartsch XX, no. 7
Inv. No. 55.15

BECKMANN, Max
German, 1884-1950

Self-portrait with stylus

Drypoint, 1917
J. Hofmaier, *Max Beckmann. Catalogue raisonné of his prints*, I, 1990, no. 105
Inv. No. 98.5

BELLA, Stefano della
Italian, 1610-64

The Feast of Corpus Christi

Etching
A. de Vesme, *Stefano della Bella* (ed. P. D. Massar), 1971, no. 73
Inv. No. 55.6

Les cinq morts

Etchings
A. de Vesme, *op. cit.*, nos 87-91
Inv. Nos. 55.5/1-5

BELLANGÉ, Hippolyte
French, 1800-66

The entry of Bonaparte into Milan

Lithograph, 1822
J. Adeline, *Hippolyte Bellangé et son oeuvre*, 1880, p. 228, no. 335
Inv. No. 73.1
[See also Paintings, p. 12]

BERCHEM, Claes Pietersz.
Dutch, 1620-83

The piping shepherd by the well

Etching, 1652
Hollstein, no. 8
Inv. No. 59.8

BESNARD, Albert
French 1849-1934

Auguste Rodin

Etching, 1900
Delteil, no. 130
Inv. No. 62.2

BISCAINO, Bartolommeo
Italian, 1632-57

Salome

Etching
Bartsch XXI, no. 12
Inv. No. 66.6

Holy Family

Etching
Bartsch XXI, no. 16
Inv. No. 67.3

BOL, Ferdinand
Dutch, 1616-80

Abraham's Sacrifice

Etching
Hollstein, no. 1
Inv. No. 56.15

BOLDRINI, Niccolo
Italian, 1510-after 1566

Three monkeys imitating the statue of Laocoön

Woodcut after Titian, 1545
F. Mauroner, *Le incisioni di Tiziano*, 1943, no. 20
Inv. No. 61.11

BOLSWERT, Schelte Adamsz.
Flemish, c. 1586-1659

Stormy landscape with Philemon and Baucis

Engraving after Rubens
Hollstein, no. 289
Inv. No. 97.1

A flat Flemish landscape with clouds

Engraving after Rubens
Hollstein, no. 318 (before figures)
Inv. No. 99.2a
[See Paintings, Rubens, p. 50].

A flat Flemish landscape with clouds and figures

Engraving after Rubens
Hollstein, no. 318 (with figures)
Inv. No. 99.2b
[See Paintings, Rubens, p. 50]

BONASONE, Giulio
Italian, c. 1498-c. 1580

Judith departing for Bethulia

Engraving after Michelangelo
Bartsch XV, no. 9
Inv. No. 58.12

The chastising of Cupid

Engraving, 1563
Bartsch XV, no. 101
Inv. No. 58.13

Mercury surprising the family of Herse

Etching with engraving
Bartsch XV, no. 102
Inv. No. 58.14

BOTH, Jan
Dutch, c. 1610-52

The mule driver

Etching
Hollstein, no. 6
Inv. No. 55.21

CALLOT, Jacques
French, 1592-1635

The Battle of Avigliano

Engraving
J. Lieure, *Jacques Callot. Catalogue de
l'oeuvre gravé*, III, 1927, no. 663
Inv. No. 55.7

View of the Louvre

Etching
J. Lieure, *op. cit.*, no. 667
Inv. No. 54.8

CARPIONI, Giulio
Italian, 1611-74

Moderation

Etching
Bartsch XX, no. 13
Inv. No. 58.16

CASTIGLIONE, Giovanni Benedetto
Italian, 1609-64

The Raising of Lazarus

Etching
Bartsch XXI, no. 6
Inv. No. 55.2

*The discovery of the bodies of Saints Peter
and Paul*

Etching
Bartsch XXI, no. 14
Inv. No. 57.5

[CASTIGLIONE, Giovanni Benedetto]
*God the Father regarding the Infant
Christ*

Etching
Bartsch XXI, no. 11
Inv. No. 91.3

CASTIGLIONE, Salvatore
Italian, 1620-76

The Raising of Lazarus

Etching, 1645
Bartsch XXI, p. 43
Inv. No. 67.4

CÉZANNE, Paul
French, 1839-1906

Guillaumin with the hanged man

Etching, 1873
L. Venturi, *Cézanne. Son art, son oeuvre*,
1936, no. 1159
Inv. No. 59.2

Self portrait

Lithograph, 1896/7
L. Venturi, *op. cit.*, no. 1158
Inv. No. 92.3

CHASSÉRIAU, Théodore
French, 1819-56

Apollo and Daphne

Lithograph, 1844
M. Sandoz, *Théodore Chassériau*, 1974,
no. 269
Inv. No. 57.6

CLAUDE Gellée, called Le Lorrain
French, 1600-82

Sunrise

Etching
Robert-Dumesnil, I, no. 15
Inv. No. 39.3

COCK, Hieronymus
Flemish, c. 1510-70

Mercury and Argus

Etching
Hollstein, no. 13
Inv. No. 57.7

Apollo and Daphne

Etching
Hollstein, no. 15
Inv. No. 57.8

CORINTH, Lovis
German, 1858-1925

Christ on the Cross

Woodcut, 1919
K. Schwarz, *Das graphische Werk von
Lovis Corinth*, 1985, no. H374
Inv. No. 94.3

CROME, John
British, 1768-1821

Mousehold Heath

Etching
N. Goldberg, *John Crome the elder*, 1978,
no. 214
Inv. No. 66.7

DAUBIGNY, Charles-François
French, 1817-78

The satyr

Etching, 1850
Delteil, no. 73
Inv. No. 66.2

The beach at Villerville

Etching
Delteil, no. 88
Inv. No. 66.3

The children in the cart

Etching, 1861
Delteil, no. 102
Inv. No. 66.4

Interior of an inn

Etching, 1861
Delteil, no. 107
Inv. No. 66.5

DAUMIER, Honoré
French, 1808-1879

Embrassons-nous

Lithograph, 1867
Delteil, no. 3602
Inv. No. 96.6

*Et pendant ce temps-là ils continuent à
affirmer qu'elle ne s'est jamais mieux portée*

Lithograph, 1872
Delteil, no. 3937
Inv. No. 96.7

DELACROIX, Ferdinand-Victor-
Eugène
French, 1798-1863

A wild horse

Lithograph, 1828
Delteil, no. 78
Inv. No. 60.7

Lion devouring a horse

Lithograph, 1844
Delteil, no. 126
Inv. No. 55.22

DUGHET, Gaspard
French, 1615-75

Four landscapes

Engravings
Robert-Dumesnil, I, nos. 1-4
Inv. Nos. 55.1/1-4

DUJARDIN, Karel
Dutch, 1622-78

The shepherdess talking to her dog

Etching, 1653
Hollstein, no. 31
Inv. No. 57.9

The etchings of Dujardin

52 etchings bound in a small 18th-century
folio
Hollstein, nos. 1-52
Inv. Nos. 58.10 (1-52)

DÜRER, Albrecht
German, 1471-1528

St Christopher

Engraving, 1521
F. Hollstein, *German engravings, etchings
and woodcuts*, 1953-, VII, no. 52
Inv. No. 39.4

The Vision of the Seven Candlesticks

Woodcut, 1511
F. Hollstein, *op. cit.*, no. 165
Inv. No. 56.1

St John devouring the Book

Woodcut, 1498
F. Hollstein, *op. cit.*, no. 172
Inv. No. 56.2

The Death of the Virgin

Woodcut, 1510
F. Hollstein, *op. cit.*, no. 205
Inv. No. 56.20

[DÜRER, Albrecht]
*The Assumption and Coronation
of the Virgin*
Woodcut, 1510
F. Hollstein, *op. cit.*, no. 206
Inv. No. 56.21

The bath house
Woodcut
F. Hollstein, *op. cit.*, no. 266
Inv. No. 68.4

DYCK, Anthony van
Flemish, 1599-1641

Ecce Homo
Etching, with burin work by (?) Lucas
Vorsterman I
Hollstein, no. 28
Inv. No. 97.2

DYCK, Daniel van den
Flemish, c. 1610-70

Diana and Endymion
Etching
Hollstein, no. 8
Inv. No. 61.12

ERNST, Max
German, 1891-1976

Birds in Green, Rain
Etching with aquatint and mixed techniques
printed in colours, 1959
W. Spiess & H. Lippien, *Max Ernst: das
graphische Werk*, 1975, no. 74
Inv. No. 95.1

EVERDINGEN, Allart van
Dutch, 1621-75

The two floating logs
Etching
Hollstein, no. 56
Inv. No. 57.10

FANELLI, Francesco
Italian, before 1608-c. 1665

Varie architecture
Title-page and 16 engraved plates
D. Guilmard, *Les maîtres ornemanistes*,
1880, p. 320 (Une suite de quinze pièces)
Inv. Nos. 62.5/1-17

FARINATI, Orazio
Italian, 1559-after 1616
The Madonna and Child with St John the Baptist
Etching after Paolo Farinati
Bartsch XVI, no. 3
Inv. No. 91.4

FLORENTINE
St Jerome in the wilderness
Engraving, c. 1500
A. M. Hind, *Early Italian engraving*, I,
1938, p. 48, no. 58
Inv. No. 59.7

GALLE, Philip
Dutch, 1537-1612
The story of the Prodigal Son
6 engravings after M. van Heemskerck, 1562
Hollstein, nos. 147-52
Inv. Nos. 64.7/1-6

GÉRICAULT, Jean-Louis-André-Théodore
French, 1791-1824
The Flemish farrier
Lithograph, 1821
Delteil, no. 33
Inv. No. 93.1

GHISI, Giorgio
Italian, 1520/4-82
An allegory of life ('The dream of Raphael')
Engraving, 1561
Bartsch XV, no. 67
Inv. No. 55.8

GOLTZIUS, Hendrik
Dutch, 1558-1617
*The companions of Cadmus devoured by
the dragon*
Engraving after Cornelis van Haarlem, 1588
Hollstein, no. 310
Inv. No. 56.11

GOUDT, Hendrik
Dutch, 1585-1630
The Flight into Egypt
Etching after Elsheimer, 1613
Hollstein, no. 3
Inv. No. 55.4

The mocking of Ceres
Etching with engraving after Elsheimer, 1610
Hollstein, no. 5
Inv. No. 55.19

[GOUDT, Hendrik]

Aurora

Etching with engraving after Elsheimer, 1613
Hollstein, no. 7
Inv. No. 65.4

GOYA, Francisco de
Spanish, 1746-1828

The dwarf El Primo

Etching after Velázquez, 1778
Delteil, no. 19
Inv. No. 58.6

'Don't scream, silly'

Etching with aquatint and drypoint, plate 74
from *Los Caprichos*
Delteil, no. 111
Inv. No. 39.5

The sacked ones

Etching with aquatint and drypoint, plate 8
from *Los Proverbios*
Delteil, no. 209
Inv. No. 56.14

Loyalty

Etching with aquatint and drypoint, plate 17
from *Los Proverbios*
Delteil, no. 218
Inv. No. 56.13

Other laws for the people

Etching with aquatint and drypoint, additional
plate 3 from *Los Proverbios*
Delteil, no. 222
Inv. No. 59.10

GREEN, Valentine
British, 1739-1813

Miravan breaking open the tomb of his
ancestors

Mezzotint after Wright of Derby, 1773
A Whitman, *Valentine Green*, 1902, no. 174
Inv. No. 98.2

GUCHT, Gerard van der
Anglo-Flemish, 1696-1776

Tancred and Erminia

Engraving after Poussin
A. Andresen, *Nicolas Poussin [...]*
Kupferstiche, 1863, no. 414
Inv. No. 39.19
[See also Paintings, Poussin, p. 44]

HEERSCHOP, Hendrik
Dutch, c. 1620/1-after 1672

A hermit seated under a roof

Etching, 1652
Hollstein, no. 5
Inv. No. 65.5

HOLLAR, Wenceslaus
Bohemian, 1606-77

Queen Henrietta Maria

Etching after Van Dyck, 1641
G. Parthey, *Wenzel Hollar, beshreibendes*
Verzeichniss seiner Kupferstiche, 1853, no. 1537
Inv. No. 91.5

Muscarum scarabeorum vermiumque variae
figurae et formae

9 etchings from the set of 12, 1646
G. Parthey, *op. cit.*, nos. 2165-7, 2169-71, 2173-5
Inv. Nos. 98.1/1-9

INGRES, Jean-Auguste-Dominique
French, 1780-1867

Lady Glenbervie

Lithograph, 1815
Delteil, no. 3
Inv. No. 57.1

The Hon. Frederick Sylvester Douglas

Lithograph, 1815
Delteil, no. 5
Inv. No. 64.2

JACKSON, John Baptist
British, 1701-c. 1780

Christ on the Mount of Olives

Chiaroscuro woodcut after Jacopo Bassano
Le Blanc, no. 8
Inv. No. 58.1

JODE, Pieter de, the younger
Flemish, 1601-after 1674

Christ with Nicodemus

Engraving after Gerard Seghers
Hollstein, no. 12
Inv. No. 96.2

KAPP, Edmond Xavier
British, 1890-1978

Madame Eidenschenk-Patin

Lithograph
Inv. No. 70.5

Pablo Picasso

Lithograph
Inv. No. 69.9/242

KLINGER, Max
German, 1857-1920
The philosopher
Etching with aquatint, 1910
H. W. Singer, *Max Klingers Radierungen,
Stiche und Steindrücke*, 1905, no. 232
Inv. No. 92.1

KOLBE, Carl Wilhelm
German, 1759-1835
*A youth playing the lyre to a maiden at a
fountain in luxuriant vegetation*
Etching, 1802/3
U. Martens, *Der Zeichner und Radierer
C. W. Kolbe d. Ä.*, 1976, no. 95
Inv. No. 92.6

KOLLWITZ, Käthe
German, 1867-1945
Help Russia
Lithograph, 1921
A. Klipstein, *Käthe Kollwitz Verzeichnis des
graphischen Werkes [...]*, 1955, no. 154
Inv. No. 91.1

LEBAS, Jacques-Philippe
French, 1707-83
Le négligé
Engraving after Chardin, 1741
Le Blanc, no. 222
Inv. No. 39.6

LEECH, John
British, 1817-64
Mr Briggs contemplates a day's fishing
Coloured etching
Inv. No. 44.8
[See also Drawings, p. 73]
Hunting, Incidents of 'The Noble Science'
Ten lithographs, published 1865
S. Houfe, *John Leech and the Victorian scene*,
1984, no. 156
Inv. Nos. 44.6/1-10

LE FEBVRE, Valentin and others
Flemish, 1642-80/2
Raccolta di opere scelte
Title page and 59 engravings after mainly
Venetian paintings published by Teodoro
Viero, Venice, 1786.
Inv. Nos. 56.10/1-60
The majority of the plates are by Le Febvre,
S. Maniago, A. Zucchi, and P. Monaco.

LEONI, Ottavio
Italian, c. 1587-1630
Giovanni Battista Marino
Engraving, 1624
Bartsch XVIII, no. 30
Inv. No. 69.2

LIEVENS, Jan
Dutch, 1607-74
Jacques Gaulthier, lutanist
Etching
Hollstein, no. 23
Inv. No. 56.12

LONDONIO, Francesco
Italian, 1723-83
Two sheep with a goat and a shepherdess
Etching on blue paper with white highlights,
1759
Le Blanc, under nos. 78-93
Inv. No. 91.6
A cow and a calf with two sheep
Etching on blue paper with white highlights
Le Blanc, under nos. 78-93
Inv. No. 91.7

LUCAS, David
British, 1802-81
The lock
Mezzotint after Constable, 1834
A. Shirley, *The published mezzotints of David Lucas
after John Constable, R.A.*, 1930, no. 35.
Inv. No. 94.1

McARDELL, James
British, 1729-65
Lady Anne Dawson
Mezzotint after Reynolds, 1754
G. Goodwin, *James McArdell*, 1903, no. 35
Inv. No. 39.9

McSWINY, Owen
British, died 1754
*Tombeaux des princes, grands capitaines et
autres hommes illustres qui ont fleuri dans
la Grande Bretagne [...]*
8 engravings from the series published by
McSwiny in 1741.
Inv. Nos. 55.34/1-8

Engraved by N. Dorigny, L. Cars, L. Desplaces,
N. D. de Beauvais, B. Lépicié and J. P. Le Bas.

MANET, Édouard
French, 1832-83

Charles Baudelaire

Etching, 1865
M. Guérin, *L'oeuvre gravé de Manet*, 1944,
no. 38
Inv. No. 57.11

La guerre civile

Lithograph, 1871
M. Guérin, *op. cit.*, no. 75
Inv. No. 57.15

MARATTI, Carlo
Italian, 1625-1713

The Annunciation

Etching
Bartsch XXI, no. 2
Inv. No. 64.8

*The Madonna and Child with St Mary
Magdalene*

Etching
Bartsch XXI, no. 6
Inv No. 91.8

MASTER F. G.
German, 16th century

*Vulcan and the Cyclops forging
Cupid's arrows*

Engraving after a lost Primaticcio
Bartsch IX, no. 4
Inv. No. 69.4

MERYON, Charles
French, 1821-68

La Tour de l'Horloge, Paris

Etching, 1852
Delteil, no. 28
Inv. No. 39.7

MIEL, Jan
Flemish, 1599-1664

The shepherd with the bagpipes

Etching
Hollstein, no. 11
Inv. No. 68.1

MILLET, Jean-François
French, 1814-75

Peasant returning from the dunghill

Etching, 1855
Delteil, no. 11
Inv. No. 65.1

[MILLET, Jean-François]

The diggers

Etching
Delteil, no. 13
Inv. No. 60.9

MOEYART, Claes Cornelisz.
Dutch, 1592/3-1655

Landscape with Mercury and Battus

Etching
Hollstein, no. 26
Inv. No. 69.5

MORIN, Jean
French, c. 1590-1650

Margaret Lemon

Engraving after Van Dyck
Robert-Dumesnil, II, no. 62
Inv. No. 56.7

Omer Talon

Engraving after Champaigne
Robert-Dumesnil, II, no. 74
Inv. No. 56.4

Jacques-Auguste de Thou

Engraving after Ferdinand Elle, 1617
Robert-Dumesnil, II, no. 79
Inv. No. 56.3

MORRIS, Thomas
British, c. 1750-c. 1800

The River Dee, near Eaton Hall

Engraving after Richard Wilson, 1774
Inv. No. 97.7
[See Paintings, Wilson, p. 59]

MORTIMER, John Hamilton
British, 1741-79

27 etchings bound in a volume, dedicated
to Sir Joshua Reynolds, 1778-80
Inv. No. 55.10 (1-27)

MOYREAU, Jean
French, 1690-1762

La collation

Engraving after Watteau
Inv. No. 39.8

NANTEUIL, Robert
French, c. 1623-78

John Evelyn

Engraving
C. Petitjean and C. Wickert, *Catalogue de l'oeuvre gravé [...] Nanteuil*, I, 1925, no. 71
Inv. No. 57.2

NOLDE, Emil
German, 1867-1956

Prophet

Woodcut, 1912
G. Schiefler & C. Mosel, *Emil Nolde: das graphische Werk*, II, 1967, no. 110
Inv. No. 96.5

OSTADE, Adriaen van
Dutch, 1610-85

The child and the doll

Etching, 1679
Hollstein, no. B16
Inv. No. 48.16
[See also Drawings, p. 77]

The cobbler

Etching, 1671
Hollstein, no. B27
Inv. No. 48.19

PALMER, Samuel
British, 1805-81

The vine

Etching, 1852
R. G. Alexander, *Catalogue of the etchings of Samuel Palmer*, 1937, no. 5
Inv. No. 60.10

The cypress grove

Etching, 1883 (completed by A. H. Palmer)
R. G. Alexander, *op. cit.*, no. 15
Inv. No. 60.11

PANNEELS, Willem
Flemish, c. 1600-c. 1632

Meleager and Atalanta

Etching after Rubens
Hollstein, no. 26
Inv. No. 91.9

PASQUALINI, Giovanni Battista
Italian, active c. 1619-c. 1634

The Supper at Emmaus

Etching after Guercino, 1619
Le Blanc, no. 9
Inv. No. 91.11

PASSE, Crispin de, the younger
Dutch, c. 1597-c. 1670

L'instruction du roy en l'exercice de monter à cheval [...]

11 engravings (from the set of 60), 1629
Hollstein, no. 175
Inv. Nos. 56.17/1-11

PASSE, Magdalena van de
Dutch, c. 1600-38

Latona and the frogs

Engraving after (?) Elsheimer
Hollstein, no. 6
Inv. No. 96.3

PERRIER, François
French, 1590-1650

The Holy Family with St John the Baptist and angels

Engraving, 1633
Robert-Dumesnil, VI, no. 2
Inv. No. 91.10

PETHER, William
British, 1731-c. 1795

Drawing from the Gladiator

Mezzotint after Wright of Derby, 1769
J. C. Smith, *British mezzotinto portraits*, III, 1880, no. 45
Inv. No. 57.3

PETITOT, Eurimond
French, 1727-1801

Suite des vases [...]

A set of 32 engravings, with 3 printed folios, 1764
D. Guilmard, *Les maîtres ornemanistes*, 1880, p. 225
Inv. Nos. 61.4/1-35

PICASSO, Pablo
Spanish, 1881-1973

Bust of Jacqueline, turned to the right

Lithograph, 1958
G. Bloch, *Pablo Picasso: catalogue de l'oeuvre gravé et lithographié*, I, 1968, no. 854
Inv. No. 96.4

PIRANESI, Giovanni Battista
Italian, 1720-78

The Palazzo della Sacra Consulta

Etching with engraving from *Vedute di Roma*
A. M. Hind, *Giovanni Battista Piranesi*, 1922,
no. 22
Inv. No. 39.18

The Palazzo di Monte Citorio

Etching with engraving, 1752, from *Vedute di Roma*
A. M. Hind, *op. cit.*, no. 23
Inv. No. 39.17

The Villa d'Este, Tivoli

Etching, 1773, from *Vedute di Roma*
A. M. Hind, *op. cit.*, no. 105
Inv. No. 61.5

PIROLI, Tommaso
Italian, c. 1752-1824

Drawings faithfully copied from Nature at Naples

A bound set of 12 hand-coloured engravings
after drawings by F. Rehberg, with title-page, 1794
Le Blanc, no. 20
Inv. No. 64.6a

They represent Lady Hamilton in her celebrated
Attitudes
[See also Anonymous, p. 127]

POTTER, Paulus
Dutch, 1625-54

The cowherd

Etching, 1649
Hollstein, no. 14
Inv. No. 57.12

RAIBOLINI, Jacopo, called Francia
Italian, before 1486-1557

The Holy Family

Engraving
Bartsch XV, p. 457, no. 2
Inv. No. 58.15

RAIMONDI, Marcantonio
Italian, c. 1480-1527/34

The Massacre of the Innocents

Engraving after Raphael
Bartsch XIV, no. 20
Inv. No. 58.11

[RAIMONDI, Marcantonio]

St Paul preaching in Athens

Engraving after Raphael
Bartsch XIV, no. 44
Inv. No. 64.9

Philosophy

Engraving after Raphael
Bartsch XIV, no. 381
Inv. No. 61.13

The Life of the Virgin

16 etchings after Dürer (from a set of 17)
Bartsch XIV, nos. 621-30 and 632-7
Inv. Nos. 65.2/1-16

REMBRANDT Harmensz. van Rijn
Dutch, 1606-69

Self-portrait with Saskia

Etching, 1636
Hollstein, no. B19
Inv. No. 39.10

Christ and the Woman of Samaria

Etching with drypoint, 1658
Hollstein, no. B70
Inv. No. 41.9
[See also Drawings, p. 78]

The Death of the Virgin

Etching with drypoint. 1639
Hollstein, no. B99
Inv. No. 39.11

RENI, Guido
Italian, 1575-1642

The Deposition

Etching after Parmigianino
Bartsch XVIII, no. 46
Inv. No. 62.7

RENOIR, Pierre-Auguste
French, 1841-1919

The dance in the country

Soft-ground etching
Delteil, no. 2
Inv. No. 59.9

RIBERA, José de
Spanish, 1591-1652

Head of a man with a goitre

Etching, 1622
Bartsch XX, no. 8
Inv. No. 58.9

[RIBERA, José de]
The poet
Etching
Bartsch XX, no. 10
Inv. No. 55.17

Drunken Silenus
Etching, 1628
Bartsch XX, no. 13
Inv. No. 65.6

RICHTER, Adrian Ludwig
German, 1803-84
Genoveva and *Rübezahl*
Two etchings, 1848
J. Hoff & K. Budde, *Adrian Ludwig Richter,
Verzeichnis seines gesamten graphischen Werkes,*
1922, nos. 264 and 265
Inv. Nos. 98.3/1-2

ROBETTA, Cristofano
Italian, 1462-after 1522
Allegory of the power of Love
Engraving
Bartsch XIII, no. 25
Inv. No. 55.18

ROSA, Salvator
Italian, 1615-73
The death of Regulus
Etching
Bartsch XX, no. 9
Inv. No. 61.10

ROSSIGLIANI, Giuseppe, called Vicentino
Italian, c. 1510-after 1540
Christ curing the Lepers
Chiaroscuro woodcut after Parmigianino, 1608
Bartsch XII, p. 39, no. 15
Inv. No. 58.3

ROUAULT, Georges
French, 1871-1958
Self-portrait No. 2
Lithograph, 1926
F. Chapon, *Oeuvre gravé de Rouault,* II, 1978, no. 342
Inv. No. 96.1

ROUSSEAU, Pierre-Étienne-Théodore
French, 1812-67
Oaks among boulders
Etching, 1861
Delteil, no. 4
Inv. No. 60.13

ROWLANDSON, Thomas
British, 1756-1827
Dressing for the masquerade
Tinted etching, 1790
Published by S. W. Fores
Inv. No. 48.10
[See also Drawings, p. 80]

RUISDAEL, Jacob van
Dutch, 1628/9-82
The cottage on the hill
Etching
Hollstein, no. 3
Inv. No. 58.8

SALAMANCA, Antonio
Italian, c. 1500-62
The story of Cupid and Psyche
A set of 32 engravings after Raphael,
bound in one volume
Bartsch XV, p. 211, nos. 39-70
Inv. No. 55.11 (1-32)

SCHIELE, Egon
Austrian, 1890-1918
Crouching woman
Drypoint, 1914
O. Kallir, *Egon Schiele. The graphic work,* 1970,
no. 6b
Inv. No. 98.4

SCHMIDT-ROTTLUFF, Karl
German, 1884-1976
Mourners on the shore
Woodcut, 1914
R. Schapire, *Karl Schmidt-Rottluffs graphisches
Werk bis 1923,* 1924, no. 151
Inv. No. 97.3

SMITH, John Raphael
British, 1752-1812
Dr Richard Robinson, D.D.
Mezzotint after Reynolds, 1775
J. Frankau, *John Raphael Smith,
his life and works,* 1902, no. 292
Inv. No. 47.10
[See also Paintings, Reynolds, p. 47]

SON, Nicolas de
French, early 17th century
Garden scene with courting couples
Etching after Johann Liss
Le Blanc, no. 17
Inv. No. 56.6

SUAVIUS, Lambert
Flemish, c. 1510-67

St Bartholomew

Engraving
J. Passavant, *Le peintre-graveur*, III, 1862,
no. 9
Inv. No. 64.10

SUTHERLAND, Graham
British, 1903-80

La petite Afrique

Lithograph, 1953
R. Tassi, *Graham Sutherland, complete
graphic work*, 1978, no. 56
Inv. No. 92.4

SWANEVELT, Herman van
Dutch, c. 1600-55

Landscape with the Angel consoling Hagar

Etching
Bartsch II, no. 67
Inv. No. 68.2

TESTA, Pietro
Italian, 1611-50

An allegory of Reason

Etching
Bartsch XX, no. 33
Inv. No. 69.1

TIEPOLO, Giovanni Domenico
Italian, 1727-1804

The Flight into Egypt

24 etchings with dedication and title-page
A. de Vesme, *Le peintre-graveur italien*,
1906, no. 26; and nos. 1 and 3-27 bound in
one volume
Inv. Nos. 55.3 and 61.7 (1-25)

TOULOUSE-LAUTREC, Henri de
French, 1864-1901

Le Divan Japonais

Coloured lithograph, 1892
Delteil, no. 341
Inv. No. 57.4

TURNER, Joseph Mallord William
British, 1775-1851

The Lake of Thun

Etching, with mezzotint by C. Turner, 1808
A. J. Finberg, *The history of Turner's Liber
Studiorum*, 1924, no. 15
Inv. No. 39.16

[TURNER, Joseph Mallord William]

The Chain of the Alps from Grenoble to Chambéri

Etching, with mezzotint by W. Say, 1812
A. J. Finberg, *op. cit.*, no. 49
Inv. No. 39.13

Isleworth

Etching, with mezzotint by H. Dawe, 1819
A. J. Finberg, *op. cit.*, no. 63
Inv. No. 39.15

Isis

Etching, with mezzotint by W. Say, 1819
A. J. Finberg, *op. cit.*, no. 68
Inv. No. 39.14

VELDE, Adriaen van de
Dutch, 1636-72

A grazing cow with two sheep

Etching, 1670
Bartsch I, no. 11
Inv. No. 56.16

A shepherd and shepherdess with their flock

Etching, 1653
Bartsch I, no. 17
Inv. No. 62.3

VELDE, Jan van de
Dutch, c. 1593-1641

The Seasons

A set of 4 etchings, 1617
Le Blanc, nos. 72-5
Inv. Nos. 55.14/1-4

VLIET, Jan Joris van
Dutch, c. 1610-after 1635

The carpenter

Etching
Le Blanc, no. 37
Inv. No. 57.13

VUILLARD Édouard
French, 1868-1940

The dressmaker

Coloured lithograph
C. Roger-Marx, *L'oeuvre gravé de Vuillard*,
1948, no. 13
Inv. No. 60.3

WATERLOO, Anthonie
Flemish, 1610-90

Two travellers resting in the woods

Etching
Bartsch II, no. 123
Inv. No. 91.12

WHISTLER, James McNeill
British, 1834-1903

La vieille aux loques

Etching
E. G. Kennedy, *The etched work of Whistler*,
1910, no. 21
Inv. No. 39.12

The lime burner

Etching with drypoint, 1859
E. G. Kennedy, *op. cit.*, no. 46
Inv. No. 45.2

WOEIRIOT, Pierre
French, 1532-after 1596

The wife of Hasdrubal

Engraving
Robert-Dumesnil, XI, no. 206
Inv. No. 60.1

BOOKS

BERTOLDUS the Dominican
German, active 1350

Horologium devotionis circa vitam Christi

66 printed leaves including 36 woodcuts in a
modern stamped calf binding
Octavo, leaf size 153 x 109 mm.
Inv. No. 39.27

L. Hain, *Repertorium bibliographicum*, I,
1948, no. 2993.

Published by Johann Amerbach, Basle,
c. 1490.

GERMAN
15th century

Plenarium

207 printed leaves including full-page coloured
frontispiece and 60 smaller coloured woodcuts
in an old stamped vellum binding
Quarto, leaf size 258 x 187 mm.
Inv. No. 39.28

L. Hain, *Repertorium bibliographicum*, II,
1948, no. 6741.

Published by Anton Sorg, Augsburg, 1493.

ORBELIANI, Sulkhan-Saba

The Book of Wisdom and Lies
(translated into English by Oliver Wardrop)

Inscribed on first flyleaf: To Lady Currie from
the Translator, 1895
271 printed pages, including decorated title-page
and initials, in a vellum binding
Quarto, page size 207 x 144 mm.
Inv. No. 39.29

Printed by William Morris at the Kelmscott Press,
1894.

VITRUVIUS Pollio

De Architectura libri decem
(translated into Italian by Cesare Cesariano)

192 printed leaves including 10 full-page and 106
smaller woodcuts in an old Italian vellum binding
Folio, leaf size 404 x 268 mm.
Inv. No. 55.33

Published by Gotardo da Ponte, Como, 1521 –
the first Italian edition of Vitruvius. The woodcuts
and commentary are also by Cesare Cesariano
(c. 1476-1543).

COINS, SEALS & WEIGHTS

	Number in collection
GREEK COINS	22
ROMAN REPUBLICAN COINS c. 290-31 BC	825
ROMAN IMPERIAL COINS*	
The Principate 31 BC-AD 294	1700
The Dominate AD 294-498	1712
Alexandrian tetradrachms	1187
BYZANTINE COINS**	
Anastasius-Theodosius III AD 498-717	4545
Leo III-Nicephorus III AD 717-1081	1025
Alexius I-Constantine XI 1081-1453	1268
Coin hoards (4)	243
CRUSADER STATES	54
BARBARIAN KINGDOMS	86
ARAB-BYZANTINE COINS	75
BALKAN STATES	21
SASANIAN AND TURKMEN COINS	1683
ARMENIA AND GEORGIA	250
ANGLO-SAXON AND ENGLISH COINS	28
WESTERN MEDIEVAL COINS	75
BYZANTINE WESTERN AND ISLAMIC SEALS***	169
ROMAN AND BYZANTINE WEIGHTS	38

*   See further, N. Hampartumian and E. Taylor, *The coinage of the twelve Caesars*, 1993

**   See further, J. Kent, *A selection of Byzantine coins in the Barber Institute of Fine Arts*, 1985

*** See further, A. W. Dunn, *A handlist of the Byzantine lead seals and tokens in the Barber Institute of Fine Arts*, 1985

LADY BARBER'S COLLECTION

When Lady Barber died in 1933, some of the furnishings at Culham Court, the house near Henley-on-Thames in which she had lived for nearly forty years, were removed to the University. A number of these were later deposited in the newly built Barber Institute. From them in turn, shortly after the Second World War, a selection was made of items to be preserved as an adjunct to the collection. These are listed below.

PAINTINGS, DRAWINGS, SCULPTURE, AND PRINTS

Nestor CAMBIER: Eighteen portraits, and three drawings and pastels, of Lady Barber in various settings at Culham Court, some dated (1915, 1916, 1919), and three exhibited (Royal Academy 1916 and 1921; International Society 1922);
A pastel drawing of Sir Henry Barber;
A portrait of an unidentified widow;
A painting of an interior at Culham Court, and three others in pastel (one dated 1919, another 1924);
Three paintings of the rock garden at Culham Court (dated 1915-17);
A flower piece (dated 1931);
A pastel drawing of the Codrington Library in Oxford (dated 1931);
Drawings and pastels (one dated 1917) – including a self-portrait and projects for portraits of Lady Barber – in a sketch book otherwise filled with watercolours by Lady Barber. [This sketch book bought 1972].

George CLARE: *Still life with plums*, watercolour (dated 1866).

After Anthony van DYCK: *Portrait of James Stuart, Duke of Lennox.*

J. C. Stadler, after Joseph FARINGTON: Aquatint in colour of Culham Court (dated 1793).

Antonio MANCINI: *The peacock feather* (dated 1875).

"SEM" (Georges Marie Goursat): Two caricatures in watercolour of Sir Henry Barber, one in a morning coat (dated 1909) and one in a pink coat.

James Jebusa SHANNON: Oil sketch of Lady Barber in the Music Room at Culham Court (dated 1908); *Portrait of Lady Barber in a landscape* (exhibited Royal Academy 1912).

After Diego VELÁZQUEZ: *Portrait of Queen Mariana of Spain.*

R. G. Reeve, after William WESTALL: Aquatint in colour of Culham Court (dated 1828).

F. Derwent WOOD: Marble portrait relief of Lady Barber (dated 1913; exhibited Royal Academy 1914);
Plaster portrait relief of Sir Henry Barber (dated 1914);
Plaster model for an unexecuted War Memorial for Henley-on-Thames commissioned by Sir Henry Barber.

TAPESTRIES AND OTHER TEXTILES

An English wool tapestry cushion cover of c. 1600, with a griffin in the centre, surrounded by strapwork and flowers; ascribed to the Sheldon workshop at Barcheston Manor; J. Humphreys, *Elizabethan Sheldon tapestries*, 1929, p. 19.

A set of four English 17th-century bed-hangings embroidered with foliage; exhibited London, Lansdowne House, *English decorative art*, 1929, no. 165.

An English canvas-work picture, in silk and applied motifs, initialled M N and dated 1656, with Charles I and Henrietta Maria (?) among flowers and animals.

An English canvas-work picture, in wool and silk, of c. 1710/40, with a shepherdess and an old man in a landscape.

An English mid-17th century canvas-work picture, in wool and silk, of a fashionable young couple holding hands in a landscape, with a mansion in the background.

An English canvas-work picture in wool, of the 17th century, with an active moral allegory in a landscape.

An English canvas-work picture, in wool and silk, of the first quarter of the 18th century, with a shepherd and shepherdess in a landscape.

A Flemish (Brussels?) tapestry of the later 16th century (?), with the Parting of Anthony and Cleopatra (?).

A Flemish tapestry of the late 16th or early 17th century, with three scenes from the Life of Abraham, set in a grotesque surround; same border as the following tapestry.

A Flemish tapestry of the late 16th or early 17th century, with Hagar and the Angel, set in a grotesque surround; same border as the preceding tapestry.

A border from a Flemish tapestry of the later 17th century, with fruit and flowers between two lions.

A pair of Flemish (Brussels?) tapestry panels of the later 17th century (?), with putti holding swags of fruit and flowers.

A Flemish (Bruges) tapestry of the late 17th century, with an allegory of Geometry, one from a series of Liberal Arts, woven on designs by Cornelis Schut; J. Versyp, *Geschiedenis van der tapijtkunst te Brugge*, 1954, pp. 103 ff.

A Flemish (Brussels) tapestry of c. 1700, with the royal arms of William and Mary, woven by Jérôme le Clerc on a design by Daniel Marot (?), in wool and silk with some gold and silver; exhibited London, Victoria and Albert Museum, *William and Mary*, 1950, no. 146.

A French (Aubusson?) tapestry of the earlier 18th century, with the Finding of Moses (?).

A French (Aubusson) tapestry of the later 18th century, with lovers in a park; from a series known as the Country Sports.

A French (or English?) 18th-century tapestry panel, with a bowl of roses.

A French (or English?) 18th-century tapestry panel, with a vase of flowers.

Two panels of Persian Resht work of the 19th century, made up in silk borders for export.

A miscellaneous collection of lace and whitework including some pieces from the 17th and 18th centuries.

FURNITURE

A pair of English late 17th-century carved walnut chairs, with cane seats and cane panels in the backs.

A pair of English late 17th-century carved walnut armchairs, with cane seats and shaped cane panels in the backs.

An English late 17th century carved walnut day-bed, with cane seat and cane panel in the adjustable back.

A pair of English 18th-century walnut and parcel gilt chairs, with needlework coverings of c. 1730/50.

ALSO

Two copy-drawings by Sir Henry Barber (dated 1875); five copy-drawings by Lady Barber (one dated 1880), a number of landscapes in watercolour by her, mainly in two sketch books (probably before 1916), and two needlework pictures by her (dated 1918 and 1921).

Photographs of the Barbers, and some other photographs collected by them.